Paul Newham is a world authority on the psychology of the human voice. He has designed and implemented the only training world-wide in Voice Movement Therapy, and is the founder and director of the International Association for Voice Movement Therapy. Widely sought after as a group leader, he works as an adjunct professor, visiting lecturer and workshop leader at conservatories, universities, with the Oxford & Cambridge and Royal Society of Arts Examination Board, and at contemporary healing centres in Europe and the USA. His book *Therapeutic Voicework* has become a seminal text for courses in linguistics, speech therapy and psychotherapy. Now, for the first time, *The Healing Voice* makes his ground-breaking system available to the general public.

In addition to his academic achievements and international research, he has coached members of the Royal Shakespeare Company and the Royal Opera in Britain, as well as renowned actors and rock singers.

The

Healing Voice

How to Use the Power of Your Voice
to Bring Harmony into Your Life

PAUL NEWHAM

ELEMENT
Shaftesbury, Dorset • Boston, Massachusetts
Melbourne, Victoria

© Element Books Limited 1999
Text © Paul Newham 1999

First published in the UK in 1999 by
Element Books Limited
Shaftesbury, Dorset SP7 8BP

Published in the USA in 1999 by
Element Books, Inc.
160 North Washington Street
Boston, MA 02114

Published in Australia in 1999 by
Element Books Limited and distributed
by Penguin Australia Limited
487 Maroondah Highway, Ringwood
Victoria 3134

Cover design by Mark Slader
Text design by Dale Tomlinson
Text illustration by Paul Newham and David Woodroffe
Typeset by Footnote Graphics, Warminster, Wilts
Printed and bound in Great Britain by Biddles Ltd, Guildford & King's Lynn

British Library Cataloguing in Publication data available

Library of Congress Cataloging in Publication data available

ISBN 1 86204 548 8

DEDICATION

This book is dedicated to my dear friend Anne Brownell whose grace of touch, bountiful heart and relentless conviction to the truth of the soul is inspiring beyond measure. Without Anne I would have cowered from writing these words. She remains my compatriot in spiritual service. This book is my prayer of thanks for having been blessed with the fortune of having her cross my path.

*

Note on the exercises in this book

Vocalizing, singing and working on the voice should not cause painful physical sensations in the throat. If in the course of pursuing any of the exercises in this book you feel a burning sensation, a soreness or a discomfort you should stop what you are doing and seek professional guidance. Information and a contact address for those seeking help are given at the back of this book.

Please note that any information given in this book is not intended to replace, countermand or conflict with the advice given to you by professional healthcare or medical practitioners. Any person with a condition requiring medical attention or counselling should consult a qualified practitioner or suitable therapist.

Contents

List of Figures x

INTRODUCTION
Why the Soul Must Sing XI
*How people have changed their lives through singing
and how you can do the same*

PART ONE
The Primal Voice

CHAPTER ONE
Songs from the Cradle of Humankind 3
*How primitive peoples had a sound for everything and
how we have evolved to forget the human heart*

CHAPTER TWO
Mother's Voice, Mother's Milk II
*Why babies cry and how mothers have learned to
hold them in a sonorous embrace*

CHAPTER THREE
The Birth of Language and the Loss of Sense 21
*How language imprisons us and how
and why we need to escape*

CHAPTER FOUR
A Voice Beyond Words 32
*Why we need to voice things which cannot be spoken
and how to go about it*

PART TWO
The Physical Voice

CHAPTER FIVE
The Source of Human Sound 43
*How the voice works, why it often fails us and
how releasing it can change our lives*

CHAPTER SIX
Finding Room to Breathe 75
*How our breath affects every sound we make and why changing the
way we breathe can enhance the way we feel*

CHAPTER SEVEN
The Voice in Motion 89
*How the body sings and why moving in unfamiliar ways
can enhance the way we feel*

PART THREE
The Feeling Voice

CHAPTER EIGHT
Broken Hearts and Belly Laughs 99
*How crying and laughing are really songs in disguise
and how all feelings can and must be voiced*

CHAPTER NINE
Unlocking the Lion in our Hearts III
Why animals don't need to talk and how to voice our primal instincts

CHAPTER TEN
Prayers and Prophecies 122
*How people from all spiritual traditions have used the voice to
contact the soul and why we should do the same*

PART FOUR
The Political Voice

CHAPTER ELEVEN
Sounding Sensual 133
Why the voice is a sex organ and how it is used to attract and seduce

CHAPTER TWELVE
Noises from the Battlefield 142
*How those with power have misused the voice as a
weapon of destruction and how those who have been wounded
can recover the sounds of victory*

CHAPTER THIRTEEN
The Song of the Mermaid 147
*How the wisdom of ancient tales echoes
with the song of the sirens*

PART FIVE
The Healing Voice

CHAPTER FOURTEEN
Thou Shalt Not Cry Out Loud 161
*How singers were once healers and how history
ruined spontaneous song with rules*

CHAPTER FIFTEEN
Groans and Moans and Tender Tunes 170
*How vocal sound can soothe physical pain and
why singing can help to make us well*

CHAPTER SIXTEEN
The Sounds of the Psyche 178
*How voice can ease a troubled mind and why
singing often works better than talking*

CHAPTER SEVENTEEN
Falling Apart and Composing Our Selves 189
*How each of us is made up of many personalities and
why each one should be given a voice*

FINALE
Your Voice and Your Future 196
*How to further unchain your voice, where to find
practical guidance and what you can do next*

Glossary 199
Index 203

List of Figures

Figure 1   The voice tube 45

Figure 2   The glottis 45

Figure 3   Shut vocal cords 46

Figure 4   Understanding harmonic timbre 56

Figure 5   Flute Configuration 58

Figure 6   Clarinet Configuration 59

Figure 7   Saxophone Configuration 60

Figure 8 The facial expression of Flute Configuration 61

Figure 9 The facial expression of Clarinet Configuration 62

Figure 10 The facial expression of Saxophone Configuration 63

Figure 11 Expansion of the torso 'cylinder' 77

Figure 12 Thoracic expansion 78

Figure 13 Abdominal expansion 79

Figure 14 Clavicular expansion 79

Figure 15 Making Spherical Space 92

Figure 16 The Animal Matrix 116

Figure 17 The Prayer Cycle 127

Why the Soul Must Sing

*How people have changed their lives through singing
and how you can do the same*

This book is about the healing power of the human voice and it shows how unlocking the voice can liberate the spirit. Everybody can release their voice from constriction and constraint; and marvellous things happen to people when their voice emerges triumphantly from the silence of the years.

This book is not about speaking. It is about something more primal and elemental than that. This book is about singing. But when I speak of singing I am not referring to scales and keys or to crotchets and quavers; I am referring to the universal sound of the human voice which we used in the ancient days before language and which all babies use before they don the stifling cloak of words.

I am referring to an art that we all once possessed but of which many people have been robbed: the art of giving voice in sound to all that we feel. I am speaking of singing not as a means of entertaining a judgmental ear, but as a means of giving form and shape to the deepest parts of our souls.

Fifteen years ago I gave my first singing lesson. I began to witness the healing power of the voice and my life's mission to uncover the relationship between sound and soul commenced. Yet, in many ways it began earlier than that, when I was too young to know consciously which path I would tread.

I was born and raised in the middle of an overcrowded housing estate just north of London. My mother was of a mild and gentle nature who bonded with me in intimacy and confidence. My father was an angry and wrathful man who taught me how to rise early and work. The relationship between my parents was terrible and terrifying. My father was a heavy drinker, had hands like dinner plates and a voice which was loud as a horn and rough as sandpaper. My mother, meanwhile, lived on instant coffee and cigarettes and raised her voice only in desperation.

Throughout my young years the immediate environment was a

stage upon which my mother and father repeatedly enacted the same savage opera. Regularly, my father would return to the house, often in the middle of the night, call for my mother to descend from the bedroom and begin hollering and shouting. These thunderous baritonal yells of rage blended with the high, whimpering sobs of my mother, producing an orchestral duet with a dark and bleak ambience.

My sister and I were always keen to understand the story behind the sounds. So we would frequently place the toothbrush cup upside down on the bedroom floor and take turns to listen, hoping to discover what all the shouting was about. But alas, we could never hear the words that were being uttered, only the ferocious and intense passion with which the voices resounded.

It was not until I was an adult that I learned the suffering that both my father and mother endured as children, and was able to understand the roots of his rage and her timidity. It was not until years later that I understood my father as something more than the hungry wolf and my mother as something more than the angel at his table.

As a result of my childhood, vocal sound was familiar to me. It carried information about the heart and soul; and I needed no words to embellish and clarify the message of the voice – I understood the language of sonorous vibrations.

Later in life, when I graduated from my degree studies, I started working with handicapped people who could not speak but who produced a pandemonium of vocal sound. This work came naturally to me and the cacophonous environment was not intimidating – it was familiar. I worked for some years with all kinds of handicapped people, helping them to express themselves through vocal sound; and I developed a reputation as a specialized singing teacher for people who could not speak. Then one day, one of the ancillary care-assistants saw me teaching a simple musical tune to a handicapped boy called Jonathan at a special education centre; afterwards she asked me if I would give her a singing lesson. That was fifteen years ago.

The student was a very shy young woman called Sandra who had the idea that working on her voice might help her find more self-confidence. Within five minutes of the lesson she was awash with tears. She spent the remaining fifty-five minutes telling me her life story.

By the end of my first year as a singing teacher and voice coach I had so many clients I was working seven days a week. Those who came to work with me ranged in age from fourteen to seventy-nine.

Some could barely make an audible sound initially and were terrified of opening their mouths; others leapt in without a second thought and played freely with their voice; some were opera singers, some were pop singers; some were coming to work on their voice for the first time, others had worked with many teachers before; some were brazen and brash, others were meek and mild; some were rich, some were poor; some were physically handicapped, others were athletic and agile; some used their voice professionally in the arts, in the church, in politics or in teaching; others used their voice only when they had to. Yet they all had one thing in common. They each revealed that all was not well in their heart, in their psyche, in their soul.

After a year of working as a singing teacher and voice coach I realized that the clients I attracted were those who wanted more than to attain a good voice, a pretty voice, a functional voice or a powerful voice. My clients were those who wanted to give voice to the parts of themselves that had been driven underground by misfortune, repression, trauma and the constant struggles of life. My clients wanted to refind their spirit and they sought to do this through their voice.

As my work deepened, I learned that my approach was quite different to the usual way of working adopted by many teachers. In my sessions, the focus was on helping people to uncover the complete range of their voice and to give authentic vocal expression to the entire canvas of their being. It was not important that the sounds were musical and beautiful according to the prejudices of the Western classical ear. In my sessions, people made sounds of every shape and density, of every hue and pigment. My work was therapeutic rather than aesthetic.

The development of my therapeutic teaching was underpinned by a commitment to using my own voice as a probe with which to investigate the deepest parts of myself. Every day I worked upon my voice, taking it to corners of the acoustic soul which I had not encountered before. When I first started exploring my voice, I found it easy to sing in high pitched tones and in falsetto register; but I could not reach the deeper range of bass and baritone notes. In many ways my voice was classically feminine. I began to realize that high vocal sounds reminded me of my mother and it was joyous to embody her spirit through my voice, because I had always had very positive feelings for her. But deep tones reminded me of my father and it was terrifying to embody his essence, for I had always had very negative feelings for him. But as I gradually forged a new adult relationship with my father and came to know him as a whole person with his own vulnerabilities and tragedies, so I began to find access to my deep voice. The discovery of the connections between my voice and that of my parents was mirrored in the experiences of many of my clients whose vocal inhibitions could often be traced to their early life.

As my journey through my voice took me closer and closer to the core of my psyche, I started to conjure up feelings, images, moods and characterizations which seemed both part of me and yet at the same time beyond my personal experience. I would produce sounds which seemed to come through me as though from a domain outside of myself. It was as though a cascade of sounds poured from my soul, giving shape to a family I had never known. I felt as though I was reliving familiar experiences, remembering familiar situations, animating familiar feelings and sensations – yet in another way it was all completely new.

Then, my mother told me something which radically changed my life. My father was in fact not my father. I was conceived through artificial insemination by an anonymous donor in the early days of such research when it was shrouded in secrecy. This explained many of the images which seemed to take acoustic form through the sounds which I made. I felt that I was connecting to my genetic roots, to the psychic bloodline of which my conscious mind was ignorant but which my deeper self recalled in sound. The knowledge which my mother gave me changed my life. For it enabled me to understand how the human voice can help to reunite the soul with its lost history.

But the work on my voice went deeper than this. In time, I found myself expressing emotions of a vast and consuming magnitude in vocal sounds which seemed to encapsulate a primordial essence. I felt that I was singing the pains and pleasures of the world. I had passed beyond the personal into the archetypal and transpersonal.

Again, this was mirrored in my clients, many of whom would tap into a deep and primal part of themselves, bringing forth emotions and sensations in sound which seemed to come from a universal place, a realm of reality beyond personal experience. Because of my own personal story, I was able to relate to such people from a place of my own experience and with visceral understanding.

During their vocal journey, many of my clients would encounter a spiritual realm of experience and come to face their need to know themselves spiritually. During the very early days of my research, I was touched by the hand of Christ and continue to follow that path. Having a deep faith and belief in something so good provides me with a strong foundation as I act as a guide for others in their search. But not everybody follows the same road; and I have a deep respect and tolerance for all authentic roads to a spiritual life. I also consider myself blessed to have the opportunity to work with people from all religious persuasions and thank them for what they have taught me.

As a result of constant work on my voice, I developed a vast vocal range and began to receive many invitations to show the power and flexibility of the human voice at musical conservatories, at medical conventions, in concert halls, in theatres and at therapeutic conferences.

Over the next five years, as news of my work spread, I was approached by professionals from many different fields, including psychotherapists, laryngologists, speech therapists and those in the healing arts. The techniques which I had forged from years of training my own voice and working with individual clients from all walks of life had enabled me to synthesize a system for using singing and vocalization as a healing tool. So I began to lead short courses for professionals who approached me so that they could make use of my techniques. The name given to the method I founded was Voice Movement Therapy.

Now, years later, these short courses that I direct in Voice Movement Therapy have developed into a full professional training leading to a qualification that is accredited by the Oxford & Cambridge University and Royal Society of Arts Examinations Board. In addition to working with individual clients, I have the privilege of directing the only accredited professional training in the healing use of voice worldwide. Trainees on the course come from all over the world and there is a gradually emerging network of practitioners who use Voice Movement Therapy in various educational and therapeutic settings. However, most trainees come on to the course to experience their own healing journey through voice.

In essence, Voice Movement Therapy is very simple. The clients begin by making their most effortless natural sound whilst the practitioner listens to the acoustic tone of the voice, and examines the muscle tone of the body and the way the client breathes. In response, the practitioner may massage and manipulate the client's body, give instruction in various ways of moving, suggest moods and images which the client allows to effect and infiltrate the vocal timbre as well as helping the client understand the emotions and sensations that arise, and relating them to the client's life-journey. As a result of this process, the client's voice is able to give authentic expression to the soul. The Voice Movement Therapy practitioner will also offer an holistic system of technical training which helps the voice develop in range and malleability. As the process unfolds, the client is encouraged and enabled to use creative writing from which lyrics for songs are drawn. The practitioner then helps the client create songs which are vocalized using the broadest possible range of the voice, giving artistic expression to the deep recesses of the soul. In addition, the spectrum of voices that are elicited during the process are used as the basis from which to create characters which symbolize and express different aspects of the self. Voice Movement Therapy thereby draws on dance, music and drama and provides an holistic and integrated healing art where creative movement, creative writing, music and theatre are synthesized into a coherent strategy within which all strands are linked by the common thread of the voice. In addition, Voice Movement Therapy draws upon a physiological dimension, as the voice is so often the locus for somatic and psychosomatic difficulties. The end result of Voice Movement Therapy is that the client finds access to sounds which give expression to aspects of the self, psyche or soul which have been hidden in the dark, unseen and unheard. The effect of the work is psychologically uplifting, physically invigorating, creatively rejuvenating and serves to release the voice and the spirit from constriction and isolation. In essence, Voice Movement Therapy aims to access the healing power of the voice.

The book offers you an insight into this healing power. In it I have combined the philosophical and psychological background to the art of vocal healing with true stories of those from my consulting room who exemplify the power of the voice to rejuvenate and revive the body and soul. I am grateful to those who have allowed me to use their story, though names and some other details have been altered to preserve confidentiality. In addition, I have woven into the book a selection of exercises which will enable you to experience some of this healing power yourself. At the centre of Voice Movement Therapy is a system for understanding the voice which breaks vocal sound down into ten ingredients; and I have explained the system in this book to help you comprehend the magic of vocal alchemy. For those who wish to hear this system at work and learn further how to use it, I have produced a complete audio course called *The Singing Cure*. Information on how to obtain this course and other resources is given at the back of this book.

The Healing Voice has been fermenting in my dreams for many years and comes directly from my heart to you. I hope that it will inspire you to reclaim the part of your soul that longs to sing.

Voice Movement Therapy Exercise

Warm-up

Throughout this book you will find exercises that will enable you to extend the range and malleability of your voice as well as to use your vocal instrument as an aid to healing. To get the most from the exercises and to ensure that you look after your voice, it is best to spend a little time warming up the voice before exploring any of the specific exercises. The following is a suggested Voice Movement Therapy warm up exercise which you can use in this way.

Stand, if you are able, with your arms hanging loosely by your side. Alternatively, sit upright with your hands resting in your lap. Drop your jaw and yawn. As you breathe in and out through the mouth feel the air inflating and deflating your torso. If you experience any aches or pains, gently stretch and ease the painful part of the body. Now begin to tone on the different vowels a e i o u, feeling the vibration massaging your body from head to toe. As you vocalize, stretch your body and begin to move so that you provide vocal accompaniment to your own private dance. As you work allow your voice to rise and fall in pitch and in loudness. After five to ten minutes allow yourself to relax and give yourself a few moments in which to allow any feelings or sensation that may have arisen to be acknowledged.

PART ONE

The Primal Voice

CHAPTER ONE

Songs from the Cradle of Humankind

*How primitive peoples had a sound for everything
and how we have evolved to forget the human heart*

In the beginning

In the beginning there was no word; for the words were all with God. In the beginning there were only sounds.

In the beginning, when the first light blessed the face of the earth, when the ice broke in the north and the winds blew in the south, the first among us cried out their pains and called out their joys in song.

We sang out our feelings long before we could speak our thoughts. In ancient times, when we had barely differentiated ourselves from the other beasts in the field, our instincts poured forth in song as we cried and yelled, called and wailed.

There are times when we revert to the urgency and immediacy of these primal cries: when we are enveloped in deep sorrow or consumed with joy; when we are filled with rage or paralysed by fear. At such times words fail us and we return to a universal emergency language of voice. Most of the time, however, we wrap up safe and warm in a blanket of words which say a lot and reveal little.

Words change as cultures evolve. A word may mean one thing today and another tomorrow. But the beat of the human heart remains constant like a clock of ages. Unlike the human heart, words are not the same in all places. Every language has a different word for sorrow, joy, rage and fear. Yet the sounds of these emotions are recognizable everywhere and have remained unchanged by the centuries.

For many of us, speech fails because so much of what we feel is beyond words. Inside of us we carry a reservoir of feeling which ripples through the blood in the chambers of our heart. The language of being, no matter how replete the thesaurus of our vocabulary, will never be adequately served by speech because so much of our soul is in the realm of the unspeakable.

In the beginning there were no words; for the words were all with God. In the beginning there were sounds and movements. In the absence of words we were once great performers, sculpting our bodies

3

and orchestrating our voices to describe the day's events like singing acrobats. Through this primeval song and dance we could depict fire and rain, express triumph and defeat and tell of the flooding of the river, the careening of the bear and the charging of the bull. To communicate fear we could increase our breathing rate to a loud panting and lower our vocal pitch, combining it with a flickering muscular tremor and vocal tremolo, as we crouched down to assume a defensive bodily pose with arms covering our head. To communicate joy we could leap from the earth and raise our pitch, combining it with loud crescendos as we placed our hand upon our heart and smiled with glee. Because this song and dance demanded total bodily and vocal involvement, it was impossible to express emotions without feeling them.

But with the dawn of language, we have lost this close connection to our emotions. The word 'fear' has replaced the frightened sensations that it is supposed to represent. We do not need to give fear a voice for we have given it a word. Now we have language in our possession, we do not need to experience an emotion in order to communicate it.

When God gave humankind the gift of speech he gave us a language of the mind and we took it in celebration and delight. But in our excitement we came to forget the song of the heart.

A sound becoming

We have become creatures of words. Talking is the most frequently pursued activity in the modern world. Put two people together anywhere on the earth and within a few moments they will be exchanging words. The language of the spoken word has become the most important aspect of human communication and self-expression. Speech is the medium through which we express our selves at home, in the workplace, with our friends and with our rivals. Others come to know us through what we say and we are often judged by the words that come out of our mouth.

But in the beginning there were no words; and at this time everything sang. The stones and the river, the trees and the moon, the bear and the eagle – all these sang their serenade. When we heard the rustling of the leaves, we believed the great oak to be singing; when we heard the rushing of the waterfall, we believed that the river was singing; and when the eagle screeched and the bull bellowed, these too were heard as song. During this age of the song, we believed that everything had a soul and a spirit, for we had not yet developed the sceptical and scrutinizing eye that comes with words; and the soul of a thing was expressed through its song.

Because there were no words for bear or for river, for moon or for rain, to communicate to our friends and rivals we had to use our voice and body to express the fundamental essence of things. And when we sang the song of the bear or the river, we became one with them. During this time we lived closely with nature because whenever we sang, we became one with everything around us through a sonic embodiment. In some cultures this vocal and physical form of communication was developed into ritual singing and dancing where masks were worn, furs were draped over the body and the performers would transform into an animal and take on its qualities and powers.

No one has ever discovered a culture, a tribe or a society which does not sing. Every group of people upon this earth possesses song: from the nomadic tribes of the frozen tundra to the Aborigines of the Australian desert; from the Indians of the Peruvian forest to the Masai warriors of the Kenyan bush; from the communities of the Mongolian mountains to the explorers of North America. Singing is a universal custom and the songs of a culture express its beliefs and taboos, its worries and its victories. The communal spirit of a society is preserved in song.

Singing has always been an enlivening communal activity which has brought people together in grief and in joy, in sorrow and in jubilation. At the wedding feast and in the funeral procession, in the cotton fields and along the railroads, in the gospel halls and in the chapels, among marching soldiers and protesting prisoners, among the faithful and among those who despair – singing has, since the earliest times, released people from isolation and enabled those from all quarters of the globe to make themselves known to God and to the world. Yet, in the modern Western world, the act of singing has been sequestered by the fortunate elite who take lessons, learn scales and convince us that singing is a specialized art performed by the anointed. In fact, singing is a social and spiritual communion in which every man and woman, boy and girl has the right to take part.

The human voice is capable of producing an extremely rich diversity of sound – from the piercing screeches of the heights to the guttural belches of the depths; from wails of grief-stricken anguish to hollers of tumultuous triumph; from soft whispers of romance to hard yells of rage; from rough, gruff tones which agitate and excite to smooth, liquid notes which create a balm for the ears. This incredible range of the human voice is evident in the diverse styles of singing from different cultures around the world. Singing voices from dissimilar cultures can be so different that they barely sound like the same instrument; and a vocal sound which is honoured as a virtuous symbol of beauty in one place may be regarded as ugly and an unbearable insult to the ears in another. Yet all songs are sung by the same throat. From the twanging nasal resonance of Tuvanese folk song to the hefty calls of the blues holler; from the careful stillness of the classical Indian raga to the penetrating vibrato of classical European opera; from the violent yells of punk rock to the sweet harmonies of Bulgarian choirs – all these and more may legitimately be named singing.

Running through the acoustic fabric of all the world's voices is a universal sound common to every man and woman which rises up from the soul's core. Regardless of age, gender, race or creed, everyone has this voice, for it is the call of the heart; it is the voice which announced our arrival from womb to world.

We come into this world crying and calling, wailing and singing; and for the first months of our life all of our needs and instincts, our dissatisfactions and discoveries are immediately vocalized without apology and without censor. Then, along comes language and the oppressive demands of the family, of school and of society. For many, the road to becoming an adult involves being increasingly silenced to the point where the original call of the heart is but a dim echo in the corridors of hidden memory. Our healing begins with reclaiming this call of the heart which so many people have lost.

The sound of our calling

Though we may forget the power of our voice to call forth what we need, we do not forget the needs themselves; for they churn and simmer in the alchemical chamber of our belly where we feel the intensity of our passions. Most people would admit that in the pit of their stomach there is a yearning, a craving and a desire so great it could never be fully described in words. It is like the hunger which permeates the baby's stomach and rises up through the throat in cries of need; except that the hungers of the soul are manifold and infinite.

To redeem ourselves from the impending silence which holds us in subservience to worry, fear and dissatisfaction our first task is to recover the call of the heart. You can hear this call in many indigenous singing styles and religious ceremonies. When the Muslim muezzin calls the people to prayer from the tower – this is calling. When the Quaquali singer reaches the crescendo of his epic song or the Welsh shepherd instructs his dog on the other side of the field – this is calling. When the railroad builders and cotton-pickers projected their voices over huge distances or when the American cowboys yodelled from their ranch – this was calling.

6

Calling is impulsive, raw and undiluted by musical training regimes which often knock the edges off the voice and liquefy the sediment of the soul with a single-minded obsession with clinical pristine sounds at the expense of grit and grime. The calling voice is whole because it smells of the earth and has not been cleaned up and manufactured by a society intent on buying and selling fabrications. Calling underpins many of the world's indigenous singing styles where the vocalists are involved in an industrial activity: washing cloth, hauling sails, digging the earth, kneading bread, picking cotton. Here there is no room for contrived postures and premeditated voice production techniques. Nor are there any hands free to play instruments. Often, these singers needed to communicate to fellow workers who may have been a mile away. In such circumstances, talking would have fallen on deaf ears and shouting would have been painful to the throat as well as not being sustained enough to travel. The situation required a very particular use of the voice which was loud, communicative and pleasurable to throat and ear. From these circumstances the art of calling emerged.

Most people have never allowed themselves to call out with the full surge of their passion. Yet to call out in desire and satisfaction, to call out in despair and in gratitude, to call out in adoration and in fear – this is a human right. For many years now I have been enabling people to discover the call of their heart, from timid bank clerks to assertive police officers, from those made shy by abuse to those terrified of unleashing their own power, from those with debilitating physical handicaps to highly toned aerobics instructors. The call of the heart is something which returns to the voice and soul a primal and instinctual force which regenerates the psyche and enables us to revisit the glory of that time when, in the beginning, there were no words, for the words were all with God.

Recalling the conquering spirit

The Call of the Heart has immense healing power which, when practised and developed, can regenerate our life force and contribute to the achievement of major personal transformations. For example, David had worked in the accounts office of a major corporation for eighteen years. He had gone to work at the same time each morning and returned home at the same time each night. He had paid regularly into his pension scheme, his private health insurance plan and had kept up with all his mortgage payments. At work he had made many friends and no enemies. At home he played the loving husband and father to his wife and two children. Then, one Friday he was

7

Voice Movement Therapy Exercise

The Call of the Heart

For this exercise you need to find a place where you can make a lot of noise – a mountain peak, a forest, an empty hall or a field.

Stand comfortably with your legs a little apart and put one arm behind you as though you were going to throw a discus or a ball. Then swing the arm forward and release the illusory object imagining that it travels out into the distance and over the horizon.

As you let go of the imaginary object, release your voice in a call of 'hey' imagining that the sound is projected through space and travels as far as the object.

Now, repeat this a number of times, each time changing the note and vowel, calling, for example, 'hey', 'ho', 'ha' and 'hee' as you travel up and down your pitch range.

As you call, imagine that you are releasing different emotions each time you vocalize. Call out in triumph and defeat, loneliness and celebration, fear and rage.

When you have familiarized yourself with the calling voice, replace the act of throwing an imaginary object with a gesture that encapsulates the idea of calling from your heart. Place your hand upon your heart, breathe in as you step backwards, then release your hand as you call, imagining that it is the substance of your heart that travels out towards the horizon, carried upon the wave of your voice.

When you have practised this on one note at a time, allow your voice to journey freely, creating an improvized melody arising from the passions of your heart.

called into his manager's office at two o'clock in the afternoon. He was told to collect his private belongings from his office and not to return after the weekend. He was made redundant along with twenty other men. There had been no warning and no time to prepare.

For months afterwards David was dumbfounded, shocked and incapacitated. He could not believe that a situation which felt immovably secure could collapse before his eyes in the passing of a single moment. David's wife was pregnant and as his child-to-be-grew in her belly so the savings in the bank depleted and as each job application failed he worried about what he could do. There were so many younger men, more qualified men, more able men than he. Eventually the loss of his job spelled the loss of his manhood as he felt unable to protect his family from financial ruin. Every scheme he tried seemed to end in collapse. Promises of opportunities were dangled before his eager compliance only to end in unreturned calls and shattering disappointments. David felt he had lost his voice; no one seemed to hear him any more. On the telephone to those who may have been able to offer him employment he was frail and nervous; eventually he became too embarrassed about the way he sounded to make telephone calls. After six months, David broke down in tears on the kitchen floor. The next day he arrived in my consulting room and we began to work on his voice which had been silenced by the indignation of his recent experience.

I taught David how to call from the heart and as his arms swung, so his voice came out of him like the war cry of a warrior. The Call of the Heart enabled David to access and express the dam of fury which he felt in the face of injustice and unfairness. David called out with a sound which raged, scourged and fumed as he used his voice to unleash the unexpressed feelings of outrage which fermented beneath his cultivated rational manner; and as a result of feeling safe enough to vocalize these feelings, David began to locate his passionate determination to overcome his adversity. David's voice now resounded through my consulting room with prowess and pride. This gentle man of slim proportion and placid etiquette roared and thundered, barked and bellowed, using his voice to remobilize primitive instincts: his instinct to love and protect his family, to slaughter the opposition and to pursue opportunity as relentlessly as the lion pursues its prey. We did not spend time making job application plans or discussing career changes. We spent our time uncovering the elemental drives that David was going to need if his job applications were going to succeed. For David, the Call of the Heart had been the essential key which unlocked the rage beneath his docile acceptance and the passionate optimism beneath his sense of defeat.

Often, life hits us between the eyes with something immobilizing and unexpected and we can feel shaken to the roots of our senses. Unexpected tragedies can turn a tame man wild and a tender woman treacherous. We can be provoked to levels of rage and indignation that astonish us as we feel overtaken as though by a strange and foreign body. We can become possessed. However, often life confronts us with a calamity which ought to inflame our instincts but to which we respond with the diffident and social demure of our rational mind. We spend our time reasoning ourselves out of our furore, our frenzy and our passions because we have been taught that they will do us no good. This is what David had done. But after unleashing his instincts through sound he could apply himself to the task of relocating himself in the world of work with unsuppressible dedication.

I heard from David about three months later. He was in work and sent me a picture of his baby girl.

Reasons to call

Calling not only liberates and expands the voice; it also generates our energy, animates our instincts, elevates our spirits and excavates the courage and conviction which we need to brave the world and reach our goals. Working on the vocal instrument does not only nurture the sonorous power of the acoustic voice, it releases the soulful power of our psychological voice and increases the sound of our presence in the world. Having a voice means having impact and influence. Our voice is the means by which we make our selves known and ensure that we are heard. Our voice is the window to our soul and it is through this window that we are seen for who we really are. When we practise the Call of the Heart, we train ourselves to call attention to our true self.

Everybody has a different reason to call and each person may use the Call of the Heart to uncover the primal parts of themselves which they most need to access. I have introduced this exercise to many people throughout the years and have heard their acoustic voices develop into full-bodied, rich and resonant instruments. But more importantly, I have seen them give voice to more of themselves in the world and find the capacity to call forth the sustenance which they need from life's reservoir of healing waters.

CHAPTER TWO

Mother's Voice, Mother's Milk

*Why babies cry and how mothers have learned to
hold them in a sonorous embrace*

From womb to world

The gestating foetus is suspended in the amniotic haven of the womb.
It is enclosed and wrapped in a warm, wet pocket of darkness. In this
watery world the baby-to-be rehearses the dance of life, extending the
spine, gyrating its limbs, marking out the movements of breathing,
opening and closing its mouth, cultivating the art of yawning, acquiring
the technique of swallowing, and practising the movements that it will
need at birth and beyond. This gestation and incubation takes place in
a sanctuary of sound without light. For the growing baby hears but
does not see.

The foetus is like a giant ear and is highly sensitive to the orchestra
of acoustic movements which permeate the abdominal wall. Sound
passes through the wall of the womb and ripples the amniotic fluid,
creating sound waves that encircle the baby as the ripples on a pond
surround a pebble; these sounds encompass and envelop the baby
completely. The baby feels sound bodily as though it were touching
the entire surface of its skin. The sounds which erupt and resound in
the mother's world are echoed in the waters of the womb and etched
upon the baby's skin like a calligraphy of virgin experience.

The growing foetus is so sensitive to sound that when the baby is
newly born it can recognize the specific musical contours of the
mother tongue. A baby born to a French-speaking mother will lose
interest in suckling and express disturbance if the mother starts speaking in Russian, but will resume feeding with pleasure when the mother
resumes speaking in French. The ears of the foetus in the womb are
hugely sensitive, not only to the contours of the language spoken on
the other side of the abdominal wall, but also to emotional expressions
and atmospheres. A mother experiencing depression, anxiety or
insecurity influences the growing baby. An environment aloud with
sounds of anger and conflict is impressed upon the growing infant.
When the baby is born, it already brings with it a certain intrauterine

aural history of the world – a world which it sees for the first time but has heard and felt before.

The new-born baby passes into this world already carrying a history of forty weeks; and most of this history has been acquired through the medium of sound. The star of this constant opera is the mother, to whom the growing baby listens attentively from within the auditorium of the womb and whose voice resounds like a diva for forty weeks. When the baby emerges into the light of life, it does not meet the mother for the first time, for her voice is known. The mother's voice is woven into the fabric of the baby's psyche and continues to be a highly significant source of sensation and experience.

In the womb, the baby can hear but cannot respond. During gestation we are mute and unheard. But birth releases the baby from silence and the cry of the human voice is the first mark that the new-born infant makes upon the world. Like those who walked through the dawn of the earth when the words were with God, the young infant does not speak with words but paints with sounds, relying on the choreographic dance of the body and the melodic singing of the voice to express the nuance and cadence of feeling and sensation. The mother listens to her baby's songs and replies with her own improvised arias; and the mother's voice can be as nourishing to the baby as her milk. Babies suckle more vigorously when accompanied by the sound of their mother's voice; but when this is replaced with another voice, with recorded sounds or with instrumental music, the baby loses interest in feeding.

Suckling and singing

The newly born infant experiences one of its first and most primary instincts in the stomach; and its hunger is expressed through the emission of sound through the mouth. The baby feels an emptiness, a hollow yearning for nourishment and it is this instinct to feed which rises up from the belly and out through the voice tube in the form of a hunger cry, an imploring for food. Because our first and most frequently experienced instinct is located in the stomach, many of the subsequent instinctual feelings which we host are located in the abdomen. We tend to place our hand on our belly when we are in grief, when we are in shock, when we are consumed with exhilaration and when we are awash with sorrow. And the primary expression of these deep instinctual feelings is vocal; cries, wails, moans, chuckles, guffaws, sobs and yells seem to rise up from the belly and emerge from the mouth.

For the baby, there is a sense of a continuous tube running through the centre of the torso with a hole at both ends: one in the face and one in the buttocks. Prior to conditioning, there is little taboo surrounding what goes in and what comes out of this tube. For the young infant, food is suckled at the lips and passes down the tube into the stomach. But it is just as likely to re-emerge back through the mouth as regurgitated liquid as it is likely to be expelled from the anal opening at the other end of the body. Regurgitating food is natural for the baby and does not worry the mother; in fact it often happens as a result of the rubbing of the baby's back which the mother does to help the baby release wind. However, in time, the infant realizes that once food has passed into the body through the mouth and down the tube, it should only exit again at the opposite end. From the point when this has been recognized, a re-emission of food from the mouth is then thought to be a cause for concern: we are only sick when we are ill.

The pre-verbal infant uses the voice to express instinctive feelings and is not yet ready to articulate sounds to communicate thought. However, in time, the instinct to articulate is born and the instinctive sounds of crying, cooing and babbling lead into the formation of the first words which give expression to the formation of the first thoughts. As thought and language develop, the child begins to locate the act of thinking in the head. Indeed, most adults naturally locate the experience of thinking in their head. We touch our brow when in deep thought, but rarely when we are in deep feeling. Whereas instinctive feelings seem to rise up from the belly to emerge from the mouth as sounds, thoughts seem to descend from the head to emerge from the mouth as words. Both feelings and thoughts, then, have to pass through the throat where they feel as though they are converted to sound. This makes the throat a kind of bottleneck, a point of convergence between the two major pathways: the pathway of thoughts which descend from the head and the pathway of feelings which arise from the depths. Many people seek to travel a healing journey through their voice because their issues connect to a conflict between thought and feeling and their voice feels impeded by ambivalence and confusion regarding what they should express, vocalize, regurgitate and expel and what they should retain, silence, stomach and digest. I once worked with a man called Martin whose story epitomizes such conflict.

Martin's milk

Martin was thirty-six, he was married with two children and worked as a taxi driver. He came to me asking for help with two difficulties: a feeling of gagging which caused words to get stuck in his throat and made him 'stutter'; and ongoing recurrent headaches. Martin could not locate any single incident in his life which he could describe as severely traumatic. However, he spoke about his relationship with his father as having been a source of constant trauma. His father was a devout and extremely strict Catholic and a professor of chemistry; his other two sons were both doctors. Martin, meanwhile, said that he was considered the 'simpleton of the family'. It became obvious over the period of our work together that Martin's entire childhood had been a very unhappy one. Not only did he grow up in the shadow of his brothers' achievements, but he also had a mother who showed him little attention and no physical affection. He could not remember ever being held or cuddled or kissed by his mother; furthermore, he never saw his parents hold hands or show any physical signs of love to one another.

For many years Martin had suffered periodically from extreme headaches. He dealt with them by taking a variety of analgesics but they rarely alleviated what he described as the sensation of pressure between his temples. The headaches worsened during times of extended verbal activity; the more he 'stuttered' the more his head ached.

Martin liked his job as a taxi driver because 'on a bad day' he could 'get away' without talking to anyone; but when he did talk he felt embarrassed by his speech. The words he used to describe the way he thought that he was perceived included 'daft', 'idiotic', 'a moron' and a 'dim-wit'. It emerged that these were all words which his brothers had used against him. It also emerged gradually that Martin had associated verbal proficiency with intelligence. The fact that he had not measured up to the academic standing of his father and brothers had made him feel stupid and his vocal problem further compounded this feeling and in many ways became a symbol for it.

The most striking thing about Martin's speech pattern was the involuntary jerking movements of his head and neck during what he described as his 'stuttering'. His eyes closed, his head tilted backwards and to one side, his neck stiffened, his facial muscles contorted and his head would then jerk rhythmically and spasmodically for the duration of the interrupted sound. The look upon his face during such episodes reminded me of a baby regurgitating or expelling unwanted milk. As I asked Martin to articulate different sounds and listened to his gagging, I could not help but see him as a helpless baby being force-fed, desperately trying to spit out unwanted milk, screaming and crying and not knowing whether to swallow or spew.

When I described my image of a baby spewing unwanted milk to

Martin it prompted him to tell me a story which was instrumental in our healing work. When he was born the doctors had told his mother that he was too small and light and that she should rectify this by feeding him twelve bottles of milk per day. Martin had therefore been awakened from sleep continually as an infant and had been force-fed with milk. On asking Martin to speak of his defecating habits he admitted that he suffered from both constipation and diarrhoea and rarely had prolonged periods of normal bowel activity. With this information in mind, I heard in Martin's vocalizations the strained, contracted sounds which we all make when trying to defecate during constipated periods.

I now asked Martin to extend all the sounds on which his throat constricted and simulate the voice of a baby being forced to swallow milk that it wants to expel; and he began to compose a very authentic symphony of baby-like babbling sounds made up entirely of the noises which arose from his inability to speak. The quality of his voice moved me to tears.

Although Martin was able to make progress with this, he became extremely agitated by this work, expressing fear and worry about 'what might come out' if he opened his throat. He described feeling insecure when his throat expanded as though he was going to vomit and not be able to 'control the spillage'.

It seemed that Martin's infancy had been couched in some confusion with regard to what should 'come out' and what should 'stay in'. Firstly, he was forced to take in more milk than he desired; and his natural instinct to expel it had been quashed by a mother who had been told to force it into him. Secondly, his parents had placed great pressure on all of the children to express or 'push out' intelligent language and to digest, swallow or 'keep in' anything that might be perceived as stupid. Martin, in realizing he was not as bright or as clever as his siblings, had therefore kept quiet and when he did say something he always felt that he should have kept his words to himself. Martin's thoughts and words, like his milk, had been all stored up inside him, desperate to get out yet forced to stay in. This had led to a build-up of pressure, causing headaches and constipation which frequently transformed into unstoppable diarrhoea when he could not hold any more inside him. During his Voice Movement Therapy sessions he feared that the equivalent to diarrhoea would come flowing uncontrollably out of his mouth in the form of dirty and unwanted words and sounds. So he constricted his throat to prevent this from happening. However, this meant that all his words were constipated.

Once we had realized these connections, Martin could relax the muscles of the neck and expand the throat. In time, Martin was able to shape his voice in speaking and singing, articulating language without any gagging and without the feelings of fear and anxiety which had originated in an infantile confusion about what should be taken in and what should be expressed. By the end of his healing explorations he reported two other developments: firstly, his defecating habits became normal; secondly, the frequency of his headaches had substantially reduced.

The sonorous embrace

The mother's voice is the baby's beacon; like a fog horn perched high on the rocky cliffs, it signals the promise of a safe landing upon the shores of an unfamiliar island. In a very short space of time, the mother and baby recognize each other's voice and can easily tell them apart from all other voices. Together they sing a duet which creates a musical enclosure, an orchestral embrace, a sonorous envelope. The baby craves this sonorous envelope because it replaces the lost amniotic haven where it was supported and completely protected. Sound and water behave in similar ways, travelling multi-directionally, filling every chink and every crevice. Like water, sound encloses and enfolds us, surrounding our frame in a complete circle. We can hear a sound emanating from behind us as well as we can hear a sound which originates in front. For a baby craving the lost refuge of the womb, sound offers a gratifying alternative to the amniotic waters. Deaf babies as well as those with healthy auditory canals feel sound across the whole surface of the body. Like Beethoven, who sawed off the legs of his piano and lay upon the ground before it so he could feel the music of his invention quiver and tremor to his bones, babies are astute and alive to the physicality of sound.

When the mother holds the baby in her arms and combines her vocal serenade with the pendulum sway of her body, the sonorous embrace is intensified by the physical hold. But the mother can continue to assure the baby of her presence, even when she is out of contact and out of sight, by continuing to sing and vocalize; for while the eyes see a field of vision spanning less than 180 degrees, the ears hear an auditory landscape of 360 degrees. Through her voice the mother is all around, omnipresent, ubiquitous and enfolding.

When the mother does disappear from the ear, the baby can feel abandoned and isolated and may become highly agitated. But by listening carefully to the mother's voice, the baby learns to copy her inflections and utter little melodies which the young infant sings repeatedly as a way of holding on to the mother's calming presence. Singing becomes an acoustic source of comfort which assuages and pacifies the anxious infant and keeps the mother's voice alive in her absence. Of course, there is a shadow to every light and a discord looming behind every harmony. The relationship between mother and baby is often a din and a pandemonium; and just as the mother's voice can envelop so it can engulf and enmesh. The ever-present serenade of the mother's tones can become overbearing and eventually all babies will want to silence the source of sound that once they could not do without.

The vocal and physical relationship between mother and child moulds the child's impression of the surrounding environment. Sound makes space; and the quality of sound in a baby's environment, particularly the orchestration of the mother's voice, colours her experience of that space. Some mothers suffer from things which prevent the baby from feeling secure in the company of her voice; and we are all affected by the way in which we were held or not held by our mother's body and our mother's voice. How secure we feel in the arms of the world depends upon how safe we felt in the cradle of the mother's arms and voice.

Cradling is an essential component of the infant's sense of security and containment. Constant and responsive cradling provides a calming, secure and invulnerable arena in which the baby can find amnesty from the harsh impregnations of the world. In cradling the mother's voice and arms enclose the baby's body and soul so that the infant can experience the gift of uncompromised support, as though in cradling the mother provides a sensate and palpable experience of unconditional love. But such cradling is an ideal which many mothers may not provide and an experience which many infants never receive. Each mother plays host to a pantheon of ghosts and demons, intimidations and misgivings which fill their cradling with a current of unstable and undependable energy which the baby intuits and perceives. The mother may be under stress; she may doubt her ability to nurture; she may be in a tense and unfulfilling relationship as well as having her own emotional difficulties to deal with. And the mother's turmoil is communicated to the baby as much through the acoustic tone of her voice as through the muscle tone of her arms. A sense of insecurity, fear and agitation experienced by the mother can be communicated to the baby in specific vocal timbres, which may give the baby the impression of insecurity through an embrace that is undefined and frail, impeding the baby's own sense of security. A mother's voice that is too penetrative and abrasive may cause the baby to feel intimidated and overwhelmed. A mother's voice which is too timid may leave the baby without a sense of support. Nervousness, irritability, depression and bewilderment can turn the mother's sonata and serenade into a fragmented furore and the baby can be

Voice Movement Therapy Exercise

The Holding Voice

This is an exercise for two people; so the first step is to find someone you think you can work with. Then decide who will explore the art of cradling and who will be cradled.

In this exercise the person providing the cradling gets into a comfortable position where they feel secure, balanced and able to provide strength and sensitivity. They then begin singing, toning and vocalizing. The partner to be cradled then allows themselves to curl up in their sonorous and tactile embrace, snugly easing into their arms, pressing themselves into their lap and allowing themselves to be rocked and cuddled, soothed and solaced by the physical sway and vocal motion. The cradled one then also vocalizes in an improvised rapport. As the person being cradled moves and adjusts their position in order to remain comfortable, so the person cradling tries to respond by altering their physical and vocal expressions to maintain a firm but gentle container in which the cradled partner can feel secure, supported and held.

As a sense of relationship is established, both parties should enable a musical and choreographic improvisation to unfold, noticing the positive and negative feelings which arise in the course of the exploration.

The person providing the cradling should eventually initiate a separation by gently easing away from the cradled partner and toning down the volume of the voice, leaving the cradled one in a comfortable position on the floor.

At the end of the exploration, take some time to speak with one another, sharing the feelings which arose before exchanging roles and pursuing the task again.

burned by the voice which emerges from the mother's throat like the fire from the mouth of a dragon.

Echoes of the past

The exercise called The Holding Voice is very simple, yet it brings up elemental and primary issues in many people, particularly those who find it hard to be held or hard to offer cradling. For example, I remember working with a group of people who did this exercise with exquisite attention and changed partners many times. In this group was a young woman called June; and no matter who her partner was, she did not manage to experience the joy of being cradled. She described feeling unsafe, distrustful and tense no matter whose voice and arms she fell into. At the same time she felt uncomfortable providing positive cradling for anyone else. She felt as inadequate in her ability to provide cradling as she felt agitated in her attempt to receive cradling. When we began to explore the background to each group member's experience it transpired that June's mother had been a highly strung and over-anxious woman who doubted her own abilities to raise June. Her mother had avoided physical contact with June as much as possible and the relationship between June and her mother had been tense and uncomfortable. It was understandable that June found it so difficult to find comfort in being cradled. In addition, she doubted her ability to offer cradling to anyone else for she had no experience of it herself. Once June had made these connections, she was able to relax in the arms of another and trust being held. This then increased her confidence when it came to cradling others.

Exploring The Holding Voice enabled June to allow others to cradle her and this transformed aspects of June's life. She had always found it very hard to trust that anyone else could take care of her. Consequently, she had developed a self-sufficient outer shell which tended to give others the impression that she had everything under control. Underneath this shell June was exhausted and desperate for support. Through learning to accept physical and vocal cradling in Voice Movement Therapy, June learned to receive the cradling of people's support in her relationships with colleagues, family and friends.

In order for June to experience this healing, she, like Martin, had to recognize that the roots of her struggles originated during her infancy. Indeed, the difficulties for which many people seek healing originate in their earliest experiences and are often indigenous to their relationship with the mother. The voice is such a fundamental component of our expressive soul and its freedoms and inhibitions are shaped so early in our life that they become buried beneath the weight of all the years which have passed since the days of the cradle. Yet, when we begin working with the voice it is possible to uncover and redress the imbalances of our infancy and release the voice from constrictions which have become habitually familiar but to which we do not and should not need to succumb.

CHAPTER THREE

The Birth of Language and the Loss of Sense

*How language imprisons us and how and why we
need to escape*

My mother's tongue

The new-born baby retraces the footsteps of humanity in a few
months. For, like the earliest human beings at the dawn of civilization,
babies communicate not through words but through a vocal dance of
sound and movement.

The period of spontaneous vocalizing, during which the baby sings
out sounds which are innate and inborn, is short-lived. Soon the
infant must learn to pick and choose. She must terminate the honey-
moon of free experimentation and learn to omit some sounds and
retain others.

During the early stage of development, the infant combines consonants and vowels musically, emotionally and instinctively, scoring the
notes of a universal composition in the air with cries, burps, wheezes,
dribbles and cascading tones which erupt from the cradle like a siren.
From this experimentation the infant creates a baby-speak, a *goo-goo-
ga-ga*, a jumble-talk, a nonsense language. In other words, the baby
creates a concoction of sounds that has no linguistic meaning, yet
expresses directly the instincts and emotions of the tiny vocalist.

Though the nonsense language of the infant has no linguistic meaning, it does contain the building blocks for future speech. It is made up
of little sound units which the infant must learn to combine into his
mother's tongue, if he is to be accepted as a communicative adult in a
world of talk. When listening to a pre-verbal infant combining these
units of sound, we are aware of his or her feelings not from what is
uttered, which after all is only gobbledygook, but from the musical
way in which it is vocalized. Likewise, the infant responds not to the
linguistic content of a parent's voice, but to the pitch and tonal colour
of the sung tones. The infant's babbling is uttered instinctively,
according to a musical or tonal spontaneity in which the entire canvas
of the baby's voice, including every vowel, burp and lip-smacking pop
are all just various ways of singing to the world. However, the child's

success as a potential adult with full communicative faculty depends upon his ability to harness this vocal sound-making to a set of laws. The laws which must be obeyed are those which govern the way that spontaneous sounds are combined into words; and the words which must be spoken are those which have meaning in the immediate society which awaits the child just beyond the cradle. Our competence and our intelligence is judged by how well we can say what we mean, even if we do not mean what we say.

The transition from the universal baby-song to the acquisition of the mother tongue is achieved by a process of education. The mother, father, or person raising the child, encourages the sounds that have a place in the words of her language; meanwhile, the care giver discourages those which her particular language does not utilize, so that the unusable ones become extinct.

The rules of acquired verbal communication change from one context to another, from country to country; and some sounds are accepted in one place or language and not in another. In German, for example, many words end with 'unf', a sound which is not accepted in English. The spoken language of Arabic as well as that of German makes use of the sound 'ach' as in the name of the musical composer Bach; again this sound is not used in English. Yet, all babies from every quarter of the globe make the sounds 'ach' and 'unf' as part of their musical expression.

Through the process of training the infant's original acoustic tapestry, which uses the entire range of semi-articulate sounds available to a human voice, is reduced. Eventually, the only remaining sounds are those that are of linguistic use in the society beyond the cradle. Although on the one hand this process represents progress, it also involves a loss. For the English infant, for example, it means death to the 'unf' and the 'ach'. But there are feelings stored in those sounds. The 'unf' and the 'ach', the gurgles and the cries, the sucking sounds and the blowing sounds all carry pieces of the baby's emerging emotional soul. Now, however, the infant can no longer trust that these feelings will be conveyed through the creative play of sounds which emerge spontaneously from the voice. To secure a response, the child can no longer cry out his emotions, sing out his discomfort, call out his excitement or wail his hunger. Now, the child must translate all such moods and needs into recognizable words.

In the pre-verbal phase, vocal sounds act as a direct expression of experience. With the advent of language, words serve to describe this experience. The word 'sad' replaces the sound of sadness. The word 'joy' replaces the sound of joy. As a result, the actual experience of sadness or joy is no longer necessary to communication. The intensity of such emotions is thereby diluted, as feeling is usurped by thought and vocal sound is replaced with the spoken word. We do not need to feel what we say in order to speak it.

As we enter verbal language we are aware of the price that we pay. Pre-verbal singing seems to express our being and achieve our needs perfectly. But now we must speak clearly for our supper and there seems to be little room for our feelings in the tiny spaces between words. Sound now has no meaning unless it is channelled into speech.

Sub-text and undertones

Oral communication between adults is composed of two dimensions: voice and speech. The term 'voice' refers to the sound produced by the vibrating vocal cords. The term 'speech' refers to the shaping of these sounds into words by articulating the mouth, lips, jaw and tongue. In fact, the term 'linguistic' comes from *lingua*, the Latin word for tongue. The sound of the voice, independent of the words uttered, is composed of different ingredients such as pitch, breathiness, loudness and nasality that combine in different proportions to form a range of tonal colours or timbres; and the tonal colour of the voice acts as the messenger for our state of mind, moods, emotions and inner attitudes. Most people are quite aware that the same spoken phrase can be uttered in such a variety of voices as to communicate significantly different meanings. In the words of a common but wise adage: 'It is not what you say but the way that you say it.'

The voice dimension to oral communication reveals much about the personality of the speaker and a change in tonal colour can completely alter the meaning of the same verbal sentence, imbuing it with passivity or ferocity, ecstasy or despair. In the timbral quality of a voice you can hear the vales of depression and the peaks of excitement, you can hear the lulls of concern and self-reflection and the sharp points of provocation and attack; in it you can hear the calm tone of age and wisdom and the effervescent innocence and enthusiasm of youth; in the voice you can hear resignation, indignation, hope and despair. In short, in the voice you can hear the psyche.

Although the voice may give speech its emotional meaning, it does not necessarily simply enforce the verbal content. For example, if the speaker is in some kind of personal conflict, the two channels may carry contradictory information. This is called incongruence and often occurs when the words we choose paint a public face which disguises our true feelings. We say that we are willing to do something for a friend with a tone of voice which reveals a reluctance to help; we say that we are feeling fine whilst we are actually choked with sadness. When such an incongruence between the vocal and verbal message occurs, the voice is more likely to reveal the truth about the personality than the speech.

A common kind of incongruence can often be heard in the acoustic messages conveyed to children by their parents. I once worked with a man who was an only child and who was raised by a single mother. The mother was frail, lonely and dependent upon her son for company. Whenever the son announced that he was going out alone, to spend time with a friend or to take part in the social activities befitting his age, his mother's words would wish him well and encourage him on his way. However, her tone of voice would give Michael the impression that she really didn't want him to go. This had made it very difficult for Michael to leave his mother; even as an adult, he felt that in some way he ought to be at home looking after her. Michael found it very difficult to be clear about his needs, particularly in his relationships with women. He would want affection but convey an attitude of cold detachment; he would wish to bring a relationship to an end, but continue to humour someone, too afraid to be clear about his feelings.

There are many among us who have been raised on a staple diet of confused and ambivalent messages. As a result, we in turn can find it hard to convey a single intention or feeling. Instead, we paint one picture with the words we speak and another with our vocal intonation.

Logic and intuition

One of the reasons that incongruence between speech and voice occurs is that the logical language of our speech and the emotional music of the voice which underscores it come from two different hemispheres in the brain – as though from two different parts of our self. The neurological organization of logical processes such as speaking, counting and rationalizing are located in the left hemisphere. Non-logical processes such as emotive vocal expression, artistic creativity and fantasizing, meanwhile, are located in the right hemisphere. This is why people who have suffered a stroke may lose the ability to speak but can remember and sing songs. The ability to sing is dealt with by the right brain, while language is processed by the left brain. The sad thing is that singing often becomes a left brain activity when people learn to read and write music. Then, rather than singing remaining an improvisational, creative act with tunes and lyrics drawn from memory and inspiration, the act of singing becomes a logical and literary operation with tunes read from the crotchets and quavers upon the page.

During the pre-verbal stage, the young infant draws upon the musical and emotional centres of the right hemisphere to call out a spontaneous and intuitive sonata of sound which gives direct expression to mood, instinct and emotion. But as the child enters verbal language, the left hemisphere begins to dominate the scene and the rational code of spoken discourse replaces the aesthetic code of musical expression. In Western society the powers of the left hemisphere are held in high esteem whilst the domain of the right hemisphere is considered to be less important. Children's progress is measured in terms of how readily they are able to master logical operations, even if the logic is at odds with the senses. For example, two of the functions operated by the left hemisphere are that of mathematics and spatial geometry; and a child is rewarded for mastering these fields. Yet many of the conclusions formed by this framework have little to do with reality. Our senses tell us that if you drop a brick from 500cm above the ground it will hit the floor very quickly. But maths tells us that it must first fall half the distance, bringing it to 250cm from the floor, then half that distance, bringing it to 125cm from the ground, then half that distance, bringing it to 62.5cm from the ground and so on *ad infinitum*. According to the wisdom of left hemisphere mathematics and spatial geometry, the brick would never reach the floor but would spend forever travelling smaller and smaller distances.

In the early stages of life a child is unable to conceive that an object continues to exist when it cannot be touched, seen, heard, smelled or tasted; the child's knowledge derives from the senses. However, the child gradually realizes that objects continue to exist even when their presence can not be experienced. This realization coincides with the process of learning to name things. By attaching names and numbers to things the child can manipulate and organize the words and numerals instead of the things which they stand for. However, words are not things and numbers do not obey the reality of physical quantity. So from the moment the child becomes verbal and numerate, an abyss opens up between the intelligence of the senses and the intelligence of logic.

The wipe-out effect

When we listen to music and allow it to work upon our emotions and elicit musings and fantasies from our imagination, we are drawing on the intuitive propensity of the right hemisphere; when we sing spontaneously and create improvised melodies, we are also drawing on the instinctive creativity of the right hemisphere; and when we recall a song from memory and give it voice we are again drawing on the right hemisphere. But, when we read music from the score upon the page or write our improvised melody down with crotchets and quavers, we are using the logical capacity of the left hemisphere.

Psychologists have recently uncovered some astounding facts about what happens to young children regarding these different relationships to music. First, they took many groups of children and witnessed them playing freely with their voices and with instruments, creating their own music through improvisation and describing the atmospheres, images and feelings evoked by each others' compositions. Then they split all the groups into two. One half of each group then spent several years learning to play an instrument and acquiring the ability to write and read formal music notation. Meanwhile, the second half of each group continued to explore musical improvisation without formal music training. They discovered that those who acquired the formal musical ability of the left hemisphere lost the ability to improvise and describe the emotionality of sounds, whilst those who avoided the formal training developed advanced creative skills and an acute emotional sensitivity to sound. The term for the destruction of musical intuition as a result of formal training has been called the 'wipe-out effect'.

We all rely upon the musicality of our voice to express the emotional content of our speech; for in addition to the tonal colour of the voice, speech is articulated with a certain prosody. Prosody is the music which underpins language, it is the rise and fall in pitch which brings attitude and implication to what we say and engages the listener in a way that monotone would not. In rare situations, a change in prosody can actually change the meaning of the words. For example, take the sentence 'Jane kissed Susan's mother and then Susan kissed her.' If you speak this so that the final word 'her' is uttered on the same note as the preceding word 'kissed', then the sentence communicates that Susan kissed her mother. However, if you say 'Jane kissed Susan's mother and then Susan kissed *her*' so that you stress the last word and utter it on a sliding scale, the sentence communicates that Susan kissed Jane. This is an example of how prosody influences meaning. Most of the time, however, prosody does not alter meaning but brings character and emotional colour to what we say. It is the music of our speech.

Because we all rely on the music of our words to voice the emotionality of our speech, we all rely upon the intuitive potential of our right hemisphere. Yet, because we are all so overburdened with the need to master the logical aspects of life with our left hemisphere, we are victims of a wipe-out effect. The irrational, instinctive, spontaneous emotional parts of ourselves get wiped out by the stringent and punctilious code of logic. The effect is that we lose most of our innate musicality and bury the sonatas of the heart, retaining only that small vestige of melody that we need to bring prosody to our speech. Singing, which for the infant is the most natural form of expression, becomes charged and laden with fear and trepidation. Singing becomes something that we have to learn to do. Yet, originally it was an instinct which we all possessed. Fortunately, however, instincts cannot be completely wiped out; they can only be driven underground.

Our healing journey involves uncovering the original instinct to sing and recalling the song of the soul. It is important for us to remember that the composition of song is a gift which we were all blessed with and one of the ways to retrieve it is to take the prosody of the spoken word and turn it back into melody, which is where it originates from in the first place. For we sung out our feelings long before we spoke our thoughts.

A mother's needs

Just as a child's needs are directed towards the mother, so too every mother has needs which she hopes her child will fulfil. Every mother wants something from the baby she nurtures.

Voice Movement Therapy Exercise

From Prosody to Melody

Write down a series of lines. It can be a poem or a letter to someone or just a string of thoughts.

Read the lines the first time in your usual speaking voice. Then read the lines a second time listening carefully to the prosody of your voice. Now read the lines a third time exaggerating and amplifying its prosody, creating a form of expression midway between speech and song. Now, read the lines a fourth time allowing the prosody to transform fully into a melody. Finally, sing your lines, celebrating the original song which you have created.

27

Teri came to me because she felt her voice was too high in pitch, too breathy and too childlike. She worked as a clerk at a law firm and a number of her colleagues had told her that her voice sounded childish. She had applied for the promotion due to her three times; and three times she had failed. Had she been awarded the post she sought, for which she was amply experienced and qualified, it would have involved a considerable amount of telephone contact with clients. She felt that the sound of her voice was the main reason that she had missed promotion.

Teri had come to see me in the hope that I might be able to lower the pitch of her voice and enable her to sound 'more mature'. At the same time she was a little worried because her boyfriend liked her voice and she was concerned that she might lose his affections if her voice changed too much.

As Teri explained her story I noticed that her speaking voice did create the impression of naïvety and susceptibility; and her entire demeanour was very pubescent. This was compounded by her short summer frock, her pink shoes and her long blonde hair which hung in pigtails tied with ribbons. When Teri began to sing a long continuous note I noticed that she placed her hands together in front of her and protruded her hips to one side. As I listened and watched she reminded me of Marilyn Monroe, whom she said she had always admired.

Teri's parents had separated when she was eight years old and she had always lived with her father, visiting her mother for one day twice a month. Her mother had been an alcoholic as well as suffering from intermittent mental illness. Teri had therefore lived alone with her father from the age of twelve until she left home at eighteen. Teri loved her father; she almost idolized him. He had protected her, cherished her, doted on her every smile, succumbed to her every wish and provided for her every need – so long as she remained his little girl. When she reached adolescence and began to want the freedom to explore the world beyond the exclusivity of the paternal dotage, her father had not been so good at letting her go as he had been at keeping her near.

In preparation for the next session I asked Teri to find two songs which reflected some of the aspects of her healing journey. The next session she returned with 'My Heart Belongs to Daddy' – immortal-ized by Marilyn Monroe – which she had practised to the gleeful and supporting admiration of her boyfriend and 'Come on Baby Light my Fire', which her boyfriend had said was 'too low and too aggressive' for her. When she sang 'My Heart Belongs to Daddy' her natural light, frivolous, pubescent voice effervesced as she imbued the song with the tantalizing manner of a coquette. When it came to 'Come on Baby Light my Fire' she had more difficulty at first because she could not lower the pitch of her voice and create the deep resonant tonal colour that she wanted. So I asked her to go in the opposite direction and to sing it extremely high in an exaggerated childlike voice, as though the young girl inside her was protesting in a tantrum of indignation and demand. As Teri sang the song I kept enabling her to go a little higher. With each ascending note, Teri's persona became more unruly as she located her indomitable spirit. I suggested to her that we seemed to be uncovering the defiant and recalcitrant juvenile behind the pliable damsel. As she sang higher and higher so she became rambunctious and intemperate, her arms splayed like the wings of an eagle, her lips curled back to expose the gnashing of her teeth. Each word of the song pierced through my consulting room like a series of gold darts.

When we paused, Teri was both enlivened and disturbed. She said that she had never in all her life expressed such power, such wildness and such vitality. But she said that she felt very scared because finding this part of herself reminded Teri of her mother. Teri had not only been overprotected and mollycoddled by a father who wanted his daughter to remain his princess and replace the sweet wife he had lost to wild abandon, she had also been discouraged from expressing any kind of voracious or intemperate feelings because it reminded her father too much of Teri's mother. In fact, Teri recalled a number of times when her father had told her that if she continued to 'behave that way' she would 'end up' like her mother. In many ways, Teri kept herself from growing up and finding the voice of a woman because her first and most potent experience of a woman was her mother who had been presented as crazy, out of control and incapable. Teri did not want to become her mother, so she played into the hands of her father and remained a little girl and from here she went into the lap of her boyfriend who was twelve years older than her and who encouraged the same childlike parts of her.

As Teri and I began to fit the pieces together she burst into tears of fury and began yelling at her mother: 'Where were you? Where were you?' Her breathing became deeper and her face was awash with tears as I heard her voice drop by at least an octave. This was the voice she had been looking for.

I asked Teri to write some spontaneous lyrics for a song which expressed the feelings behind her tears. She wrote:

In your mad attic far away from me
I cannot reach you though you're always in my dreams
With your eyes glazed and your tongue wild
My father keeps you hidden in case you infect me
I want to grow up not to be like you
But I don't know who you are and miss you every day
Mother won't you come and rescue me
Better to be crazy in your arms than sanely on my own
I'm lonely and afraid though father loves me so
Where were you, where are you, it's not fair you had to go

As she read the song over and over, she turned the prosody of her speech into a melody. She now sang the song in a deep exuberant and ebullient tone which washed through the consulting room like a river of molten chocolate. Her hands rested upon her belly as the tonal colour of her voice became increasingly sumptuous and rotund. This was a voice which crackled with the sediment of a mature red wine; this was a voice with the power to intoxicate and ignite; this was a voice aflame with fire.

Teri had discovered that she could release the voice of her matured invincible spirit without going mad; she had realized that though her father loved her he had also belittled her; and she declared that her vocal telephone manner would not be quite the same again. During the time I worked with Teri two things occurred. She was promoted to the post she had wanted; and she parted from her boyfriend. The one event brought her great joy; the other great sorrow. Yet Teri felt convinced that she could not grow within the confines of her boyfriend's needs any more than she had been able to transcend her girlhood within the parameters of her father's expectations. So she moved on and cleared the road ahead with a voice of depth and courage.

Changing tune

Our voice is affected by the way it is heard; and sometimes we silence a whole range and spectrum of timbral colours because those whom we love find them difficult to hear.

It is sad but true that sometimes we have to take our leave of those we love if we are to be free to voice who we really are. For if others can only love a few notes in the melody of our soul, then they cannot love us truthfully. We cannot be servants to song and give refrain only to the tunes which others require. For we need to sing the song of our own heart. But if we have the courage to change our tune and sing our own serenade, allowing all our voices to emerge, then we can open our heart to the loving ears of those who want to hear us. A true voice attracts true love. This is what Teri did and I have seen many people find the courage to change their tune and reap the fruits of walking a fresh path. It is never easy and never without sadness and loss. But once the sonorous vibrations of change have been sounded, we cannot close our ears to them though life would seem easier if we could.

CHAPTER FOUR

A Voice Beyond Words

*Why we need to sing the things which cannot be
spoken and how to go about it*

The tones of memory

Much of what there is to discover about ourselves is beyond words. It
is packed full of fury and sorrow; it is composed of volatility and fear; it
comprises elation and depression. Much of what we are cannot be
described or decoded in sentences and paragraphs. For our hearts
pound, our minds churn, our feelings clash and thunder and our souls
resound in an uproar which is both a symphony and a cacophony.
Many people – even those accomplished in the use of verbal language
– feel that they will never be able to find words to express their innermost feelings because what is going on inside them is simply beyond
words – a recognition that can give rise to a sense of complete isolation. When asked to explain, describe and articulate themselves they
are confronted with an overwhelming feeling of loneliness at the realization that words fail them. But voice and speech are not the same
and while words may fail to communicate the essence of the soul,
voice, on the other hand, can express that which speech leaves out.

Very often, people seek to heal wounds which remain from hurts
inflicted long ago. And it is not uncommon for us to perceive the scars
we bear yet fail to recall the incident which caused them. Sigmund
Freud believed that healing began when a patient could remember a
distant trauma and put the tragedy into words. Yet Freud assumed
that all our memories are capable of being recalled and articulated. He
confused the art of memory with the art of speech. For our memories
are often stored, and revived beyond the domain of speech.

Memory is aid and ambassador, scribe and assistant to healing.
Memory recollects the path we have trodden, the turns we have taken
and the map we have followed to lead us to our crossroads. Memory
makes the fleeting figures of our past reappear as contemporaries.
Memory reopens closed wounds, closes old business and repairs
unhealed misfortunes. Memory is our second chance. The powers of
our recollection can bring even the dead into our view so that we may

say what needs to be said as though touring the cemetery of our dear departed upon our knees. Our memory is an amphitheatre where the people of our lives parade in mask and costume, positioning themselves according to the choreography of our remembrance. Memory moves elliptically through time; and in our reminiscence we can replay the saga of our past over and over, adjusting narrative and interaction in our search for the true replication of what happened way back.

The word 'member' usually refers to a participant. We may be a member of a church, a political party or a therapy group. But originally the word 'member' referred to a part of the body, particularly the limbs. Thus to 'dismember' means to tear the body apart, to break it down into pieces so that it becomes unrecognizable; and to 'remember' literally means to put the body back together, to reassemble its pieces so that it becomes recognizable. Consequently, when we speak of memory and remembering we are not talking about an ephemeral notion of soul; we are speaking of the living body and the way that experience is scored deep into the flesh at a molecular level.

When we recall our history we re-envisage the past experience of our body and when memories flood forth they do so not in the form of incisively carved pictures but as a matrix of image, mood, emotion and sensation. Just as we could not name and describe all that is occurring to us during the original event, so our memories are often beyond words. Freud's masterful plan provided a tremendous gift to healing when he announced that uncovering the memory of buried trauma was the pinnacle of therapy. But he revealed the short-sightedness of his vision when he equated the uncovering of memory with the location of the recalled events in words. To remember means to reassemble the body and if memory has a healing function then its medicine is located in movement as well as words. But the stored emotion needs a channel through which it can be expressed, and as memories come flooding forth they may not only be articulated in words but also as primal sounds.

During the first and most formative period of life we express ourselves through sound and movement; and the gyrating of the body and the singing of the voice are intimately woven to form an archetypal and universal song and dance routine. Therefore our earliest memories and most elemental selves are preserved in patterns of movement and sound. Movement without sound is only half the story. Sound fixes and seals the transience of bodily memories. Music serves the art of recollection. Even those who have been diagnosed as senile and beyond the capacity for articulate recollections will awaken to the sound of a recognizable tune.

The word 'music' comes from the ancient Greeks who believed in the Muses, goddesses they believed were responsible for blessing humans with moments of inspiration. The Muses were the daughters of Zeus, king of the gods, and their mother was Mnemosyne, which means memory. For the Greeks, music had the power to revive memory. But music was also a spell which could cause people to mislay their troubles and forget who they were. For memory is a double-edged sword. Memory can only exist alongside the possibility of forgetting. Just as many people seek the healing that comes from remembering long-lost memories, so also many people seek the healing that comes from forgetting, from laying to rest, from letting go of the all too remembered past. And sometimes, our memories are so fleeting and fragmented that we seek both a remembering and a forgetting at the same time, as though we would like to uncover what we have not yet recalled and at the same time be released from the pain evoked by what we have remembered.

Because of the intimate relationship between voice, music, body and memory, working through the art of Voice Movement Therapy provides an opportunity to discover the healing power of forgetting and remembering. Those things which are buried in the forgotten backwaters of the psyche can be brought into light through sound and movement, and the pain which they bring with them can be transmuted and forgotten through song.

Memory and forgetting occupy particularly significant places when it comes to healing the consequences of specific traumatic events which are often too painful to forget and yet too overwhelming to be left wandering through the psyche and living body without a place where they can be left and forgotten. One of the psychological functions of the song in such circumstances is to provide a container for the emotions associated with the trauma. Songs retrieve our feelings from repression but at the same time they encapsulate them so that they do not hinder our spirit. In singing we recollect our sorrows and release them into the atmosphere as vocalized air. The song is a remembering and a forgetting at the same time.

Singing the soul back home

I have been privileged to hear many people create Memory Songs; but one particular example remains very potent in my own memory. The song was called 'I Heard the Plane Come Down' and was written

Voice Movement Therapy Exercise

The Memory Song

Begin by standing comfortably and allow your breathing to deepen so that you feel the stream of breath running down into your torso. Empty your mind of the day's concerns and focus on the sensations in your body. Begin to muse around the contours of your past and settle on a particular event that you wish to explore. Notice now what happens in your body as you begin to remember this event.

As you recollect the event and feel the emotions associated with it make themselves known in your body, allow the sensations to inspire you to move, as though dancing to the music of your memory.

After the dance, take a pen and paper and write a series of lyrics which encapsulate your memory and read it aloud listening to the prosody of your speech. Then let this prosody become amplified so that you discover the melody of the song. As you sing your memory song, notice what happens to your emotions and the sensations in your body.

Put the song away somewhere safe. In a few days, come back to it and sing it again, noticing how the song elicits some of the emotions associated with the original memory that inspired it, yet, leaves you free from being dominated by these emotions after the song is sung.

by a man called Richard who was one of a few who had survived an aeroplane crash. Though remarkably he had not sustained any serious physical injury, the event had severe psychological consequences. His symptoms included insomnia, nightmares, periods of suicidal depression and panic attacks. Prior to the accident he had been married and held a job carrying considerable responsibility at a merchant bank. However, he had never returned to work and one year after the accident he was divorced.

The only optical memory which Richard had of the plane crash was seeing the head of the person sitting next to him separate from his body. The rest was, he said, 'complete darkness' until he was placed upon a stretcher by the medical team.

Before the accident, Richard had been an outspoken person with a loud and resonant voice. Now his speaking voice was almost a whisper and he felt nervous when called upon to speak up for himself. Our work together began very simply. Richard sat in a chair with his eyes closed and allowed his breath to deepen. He then began vocalizing, rising and descending in pitch, listening for subtle changes in tonal colour. He would then begin to recall the accident in his mind's eye and sing any recollections which he had. As Richard recalled, I wrote down what he sang.

At the end of the session I gave Richard the lines which I had recorded and he sang them, allowing the melody to emerge naturally from the prosody of the words. He sang:

> I heard the engine rumble
> I heard the plane jolt
> I heard the captain say there was a problem
> I heard the passengers cry
> I heard the woman behind me praying
> I heard the scraping of metal on tarmac
> I heard the tyres skidding
> I heard sirens whistling
> I heard someone ask if I could hear them
> I heard the plane come down

Richard then found a melody for these lyrics by amplifying the natural prosody of his speech. During our work together, Richard produced many songs relating to the accident and the process of singing them enabled him to recall and express the intensity of his emotional reactions to the accident. As a result, his voice came bursting through his faint whisper and he regained his confidence. At the same time, the songs gave him a series of containers in which to place his emotions so that he could begin to take a step forward from the trauma and reanimate parts of himself that had been living in the shadow of the accident.

I have found that this use of song is extremely useful when working with those who have been sexually abused. I worked with a woman who was repeatedly abused by her father who forced her to engage in oral sex when she was very young. Vicky lived with a permanent feeling of tightness in her throat and her voice was extremely inhibited. She said that whenever she came to project her voice or speak up about something important, she would feel a 'stickiness' in her throat, as though her voice was covered with something that made it dull and unable to flow fluidly.

During one Voice Movement Therapy session, I encouraged Vicky to move and vocalize in a way that exaggerated the feeling of restriction in the voice so that I could bring her difficulties into sharp relief. During her exploration, Vicky moved down on to the floor and curled into a kind of foetal position. Then, as she vocalized on a single tone she placed one hand around her throat and began to rub it with her fingers. She tried to produce loud, resounding sounds but could only make a tone with a quality that sounded viscous and stuck. She became so angry and frustrated that she started rolling over, first to one side and then to the other, like a baby trying to get out of its crib. She then extended the gesture of rubbing her throat, bringing her arm out in front of her and swinging it back in towards the throat as if pulling glue out of her voice box. Then she started to make 'sticking' sounds, like the sounds which children make when they pretend to be speaking underwater. She was crying profusely. After pursuing these movements for a little while she laid her arms out to the side of her which remained completely still as the rest of her body thrashed and writhed and her voice gurgled with a muffled, waterlogged sound. Later she said she had believed that if she kept pulling and pulling at her throat with her hands, eventually 'all the glue would go' and her voice would emerge fresh and unstuck. However, her arms had suddenly felt numb and lifeless and she had to stop. During her exploration she had felt in her biceps the same sensations that she had experienced when her father had held her down by her arms. Her body had *re-membered* this part of the trauma with extremely specific and localized bodily sensations.

The more Vicky physically re-enacted her original attempts to fight her way out of the oppressive clasp by kicking and splaying, the more she recapitulated the original feelings of helplessness and incarceration. And with these feelings came the voice which felt and sounded as though it was covered in glue.

Next time we worked together, Vicky allowed her body to relax and she concentrated on making tiny masticatory movements with her jaw, as though she was chewing the cud. As she indulged these minimal movements, the sound of her voice lost its glued quality and she started to feel a melting sensation in her throat and a feeling of release. The discovery of this new vocal quality brought a smile to her face and she began singing a tune which sounded like a nursery rhyme.

Vicky felt that the sensation of melting which had come from the gentle chewing movements and the soft nursery rhyme singing were an important key for her. Vicky's original violent pulling movements and gluey sounds, which came from her urgent desire to pull away the stuck sensation, seemed to be as aggressive towards herself as her father had been in his abuse. They also tended to compound and exacerbate the physical sensations and vocal sounds which she sought to transform. As she spoke about this, she began to cry at the realization that there had been nobody there to watch over her and be kind to her when she was a child. And she said that she was not very kind to herself as an adult. She felt that the exploration of kind sounds and movements would enable the glue on her voice to melt without the need to rip it off.

I now asked Vicky to continue singing the nursery rhyme tune with her newly discovered unglued voice and spontaneously write a set of lyrics to give songful form to some of the memories arising from her healing journey. I then asked her to sing them in her unstuck voice. She sang:

I can remember the feeling in my bones
When my father made me do what no child should have to do
But my arms went dead and the voice in my head
Told me to endure this sight obscene
I was only little with no real choice
Oh please God let me take the glue from my voice
I have tried to fight and punch and kick
To expel from my throat the glue that makes my voice stick
But the more I try the more I cry
And I choke and spew and people wonder why
For Dad is dead and no one gets
Why my voice is stuck and why I seem upset
But if I feel quite safe and no one hurts me so
I can relax my body and I start to let go
And when I do my voice unglues
And I start to hear myself afresh and anew

At the end of this rendition, Vicky recalled that after an abusive episode as she lay alone on her bed, she would often sing to herself very quietly as a way of comforting herself; it was something that no one could take from her and it gave her a place to put her distress, loneliness and shame. Now she found that singing this song fulfilled the same function. It gave her a means to release the emotions associated with her ordeal but also provided a place to put them.

Redemption songs

Many great singers have endured lifelong sufferings: they have been abused, beaten, degraded; they have lost loved ones in terrible accidents; they have fallen ill to eating disorders and disease; they have been imprisoned and enslaved. The truly great vocalist continues to sing through moments of the most intense and most personalized emotion. The singer makes her tragedies public by elevating them to the level of universal relevance. The song takes a personal event and an idiosyncratic image and turns it into an archetypal form. The singer suffers but her singing does not suffer as a result. Suffering may not be necessary in order to sing; but suffering is no reason not to sing – it is the best reason.

We cannot rewrite our history. The traumas that have befallen us in the past are etched upon our souls and no healing can rewrite history. But singing tricks history by succumbing to its immovable presence. Singing writes and rewrites the past. The song remains the same; it can be sung a million times by a million people. To sing about that which has disempowered us means that at some level we have overcome it.

Singing is our promise of redemption. Ask anyone who has been downtrodden and they will tell you straight. Singing inspires hope where all else fails. Singing loosens the chains of the enslaved, rattles the bars of the imprisoned, mobilizes the strength of the starving and defies the domination of self-appointed oppressors. Singing gives dominion to those without territory, passes time for those who await judgement and gives voice to a part of the soul which cannot be beaten, broken or beleaguered. Indentured slaves sang in the cotton fields of North America; captive hostages sang in the jails of the Middle East; Kurdish families sang as they fled across the Turkish border; British convicts sang aboard the giant vessels which transported them to Australia; teenage soldiers joined with their enemies to sing Christmas carols in the snow-drenched trenches of the First World War; abandoned children have sung themselves to sleep in the lonely and impersonal dormitories of their orphanages; incarcerated Jews sang to themselves in the cells of concentration camps; minorities of every persuasion have sung nocturnal vigils outside the Houses of Parliament; marching protesters have sung in defence of those who have been wrongly accused; and entire communities have congregated to sing in worship of their maker. Songs are sung to commemorate victory and commiserate defeat; songs are sung to celebrate birth, death, marriage and anniversary; songs are sung to protest against injustice, to honour achievement, to encapsulate history, to envision the future, to resound the sentiment of pride and to give form to rage and loathing. A song may speak of love and terror, crime and compassion. In song we can sing the unspeakable. There is not an emotion or thought, an instinct or desire which cannot be perfectly communicated through song.

PART TWO

The Physical Voice

CHAPTER FIVE

The Source of Human Sound

*How the voice works, why it often fails us and how
releasing it can change our lives*

The ingredients of voice

In my experience one of the aspects of Voice Movement Therapy which people find liberating is that no prior musical knowledge or ability is required. I have seen novices discover rich and powerful voices, and I have seen musicians uplifted by the opportunity to put aside the strictures of formal music. The system described in this chapter is truly a system for everyone. However, if some of the words or terms are unfamiliar to you, then explanations are provided in the glossary on page ooo. If you want to hear the vocal sounds described in this chapter, you can also refer to *The Singing Cure* audio course (*see* Finale).

Every human voice is produced in the same way, yet every human voice is unique. The sound of a person's voice is like an acoustic fingerprint that carries their identity; and often our reactions to someone's voice are extremely subjective. Some voices attract us and others repel; some voices make us agitated while others calm and soothe; some voices dominate with authority and others sound servile and sycophantic; some voices befriend and others contend. Yet rarely do we take the time to consider exactly what it is in a voice that provokes our reaction. Without this understanding, we cannot really transcend our subjective judgements and gain insight into the psychology of vocal sound; and the best way to understand the voice is to break it down into the separate acoustic ingredients which combine to create vocal sound and learn how these ingredients are produced.

The human voice is made up of a set of ingredients which combine in different degrees to produce an infinite range of sounds; and there are ten basic ingredients which all voices possess. Our subjective reaction to voices is usually based on a response to these ingredients, just as our reaction to food is based on a response to the taste of specific ingredients which flavour the meal. By understanding the habitual recipe that makes up our own voice, we can make changes and choices, increasing the amount of one ingredient and decreasing the presence of another as we wish. Understanding the ingredients of the voice is therefore useful as a tool with which to analyse other voices and as a guide in the evolution of our own voice towards increasing malleability.

Each vocal ingredient also carries within it a certain healing power. Just as we might choose to add or subtract specific herbs and spices to a recipe in order to create particular healing results, so the addition and subtraction of specific vocal ingredients can help to heal particular issues. However, in order to achieve this, we have to learn to access the ingredients, and this is made easier by the knowledge of how they are produced.

The ten ingredients of the voice according to the Voice Movement Therapy system are:

Loudness
Pitch
Pitch Fluctuation
Register
Harmonic Timbre
Nasality
Free Air
Attack
Disruption
Articulation

Ingredient one – loudness

Running from the lips to the lungs is a long elastic tube. This tube begins at the lips, opens out to become the mouth, curls downwards at the throat to become the pharynx which runs into the next section, known as the larynx, before turning into the trachea which, in the centre of the chest, splits into two tubes, one running into each lung. When we breathe in, air passes down this tube, inflating the lungs. When we breathe out, air passes up through this tube in the opposite direction, deflating the lungs. We shall call the part of this tube which extends from the lips to the larynx the voice tube (*see* figure 1).

Laying stretched out in the larynx are two flaps of tissue called the vocal cords. During normal breathing, the vocal cords lie at rest, one each side of the larynx, like an open pair of curtains allowing air to pass freely through a window. The window between the two vocal cords through which the air passes is called the glottis (*see* figure 2).

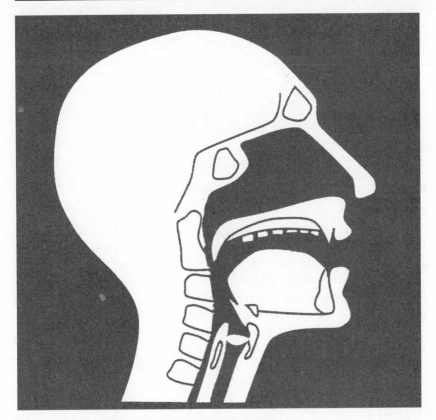

Figure 1 **The voice tube**

There are times, however, when we draw these vocal cords tightly shut, preventing air from passing through the tube in either direction. We often do this momentarily when lifting or moving a heavy object (*see* figure 3).

Figure 2 **The glottis**

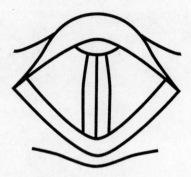

Figure 3 **Shut vocal cords**

The sound of the human voice is produced by the very rapid opening and closing of the vocal cords hundreds of times per second; this is often referred to as the vibration of the vocal cords. During this vibration the two vocal cords hit each other regularly like two hands clapping at great speed. When the vocal cords vibrate in this way they produce a note, just as a string gives off a note when it vibrates.

One of the things that causes the vocal cords to vibrate is the pressure of breath released from the lungs when we expire, just as the wind may cause a pair of curtains to flap and give off a sound at an open window. Because the vocal cords are opening and closing many times a second, the expired air is released in a series of infinitesimal puffs; and these puffs of air form a sound wave which carries the tone produced by the vocal cords through the voice tube and out through the mouth.

An increase in the pressure of breath travelling up from the lungs causes the vocal cords to vibrate with greater force, so that they hit each other harder. This produces a louder sound – just as an increase in the force and pressure of a wind would cause a pair of curtains to flap harder and louder at a window. To increase the pressure of the breath travelling up from the lungs through the voice tube, we have to contract the muscles of the chest and abdomen, squeezing the lungs empty with forceful pressure. This increases the Loudness of the voice by causing the vocal cords to hit into each other harder. To decrease the pressure of the breath, we have to ease off the force with which we contract the breathing muscles, squeezing the lungs more gently; and this decreases the Loudness of the voice by causing the vocal cords to hit into each other more softly.

The first ingredient of the human voice is therefore Loudness, which is perceived on a spectrum from loud to quiet.

The healing power of loudness

The physical reasons that cause a person to have a loud or a quiet voice are connected to the use of the muscles which empty the lungs. But there are often psychological reasons why the muscles are employed in a particular way in the first place.

The quiet voice is often the sound of wisdom; and those with quiet voices may have reached a point where they do not need to make a loud noise, for they rest easily with their insight and are not driven to prove anything. The quiet voice is also equivalent to a soft touch; and some people maintain a voice which touches gently because that is how they wish to be touched. People with quiet voices may be emotionally bruised or sore; and in vocalizing softly they may be asking for a tender voice in return to bandage the wounds of their heart. Many people who come to experience a healing vocal journey and who find it difficult to produce a loud voice have been assaulted by the insensitive vocal Loudness of their parents, partners or other individuals; and they are often frightened of producing a loud voice for fear of becoming like them. In many situations, extreme vocal Loudness is associated with negative personality traits such as being 'loudmouthed', impudent and belligerent. In fact, sounds above eighty decibels are potentially destructive to physical tissue and mental processes. However, it is a deeply healing experience to access very loud sounds and reclaim the positive side of extreme Loudness. For the loud voice is also expressive of elation, excitement, joviality, rapture, celebration and delight; and these qualities can become obscured by an over-emphasis on the negative side to Loudness. The loud voice is also one way that a person can fill space and claim their territory. The shadow side of this is that Loudness also takes space away from others. Producing a loud voice is therefore often difficult for those who find it a struggle to claim their space and their right to a distinctive territory from which to be heard.

There are many people who have no trouble with producing a loud voice and whose healing journey is more concerned with uncovering the voice of quietness. Whilst the loud voice halts a listener in their tracks, the quiet voice draws the listener in and is an invitation to intimacy and closeness. Many people develop loud and boisterous voices to mask a fear of such intimacy; and their healing journey often involves dissembling the defence around their vulnerability. Others have loud voices because they have had to shout in order to be heard above the crowd of a large family; and it is often difficult for them to believe that they will find satisfaction if they give voice to their needs

Voice Movement Therapy Exercise

Developing Loudness

Stand comfortably and breathe in and out through your mouth. Begin to vocalize on a note in the middle of your pitch range and then begin ascending and descending in steps and slides. As you do this, decrease the Loudness of your voice until you are vocalizing as quietly as possible. Now, as you ascend and descend in pitch, increase the Loudness by degrees until you are vocalizing as loud as possible. Think now of having a spectrum of Loudness from very quiet to extremely loud and take time to vocalize between these two extremes, covering all the shades between. Finally, take a simple song and sing it three times: once very quietly, once with moderate Loudness and once as loud as you can.

quietly. Others have loud voices because they were constantly made to be quiet when they were young and have developed a booming voice as a way of defying this repression.

Claiming the healing voice means restoring the complete spectrum of this ingredient from extreme Loudness to extreme quietness and using this spectrum to give voice to the heart and soul.

Ingredient two – pitch

The faster any object vibrates, the higher the note it produces. So the faster the vocal cords vibrate, the higher the Pitch of the human voice. To sing the lowest C on the piano, the vocal cords would have to vibrate 32 times per second; to sing the highest C on the piano, the vocal cords would have to vibrate 4,186 times per second.

If we wanted to produce a higher note from a vibrating string we would have to tighten it; while to lower the note we would have to slacken the string. The same principle applies to the vocal cords. If we tighten and stretch the cords they vibrate at a faster rate and produce a higher Pitch; if we slacken them they vibrate more slowly and produce a lower Pitch. But the thicker a string is, the more you have to tighten it to produce a high note. This is why the thin strings on a guitar do not have to be tightened as much as the thick strings to produce the same Pitch. The same principle applies to the human voice; and because men have thicker vocal cords than women, they have to tighten them more to achieve high notes. Conversely, it is more difficult for women to produce low notes because their vocal cords are thinner. However, the majority of factors which prevent men from singing high and women from singing low are psychological and can be overcome.

The space between two notes is called an interval; and it is the memory of the intervals between notes rather than the notes themselves which enable us to recall a song. When we sing 'Happy Birthday', we can recall the melody because we know the intervals; but the notes themselves are not fixed – we can start the song on any Pitch so long as the intervals between all the following notes are correct.

Given that Pitch is made up of vibratory frequency, the human voice can obviously sing a vast spectrum of notes by changing the speed of vocal cord vibration. But the European classical scale only classes certain frequencies as proper notes. This scale divides the potential range of frequencies into an octave of notes which we can play on the piano. But there are other notes which exist between the keys on the piano that the voice can sing even though there is no string and no hammer for that vibratory frequency on the piano.

Different cultures divide the potential Pitch range in different ways. For example, whilst Western music has an octave of eight notes, classical Indian music has a scale of twenty-two notes. What is regarded as a musical note in one place is regarded as redundant in another. But in talking rather than singing, people from all cultures are free from aligning the Pitch of their voice with a set scale and the voice rises and falls through the complete range of potential frequencies. This is why singing traditions that originate in the fields and along the railway tracks – where people extend their natural speaking voices into a call – do not suffer from the restrictions of formal music.

The second ingredient of the human voice is therefore Pitch, also referred to as 'note', which is perceived on a spectrum from low to high.

The healing power of pitch

The height and depth of a voice is dependent on the vibratory speed of the vocal cords, which is in turn dependent on their thickness and the tension of the muscles which tighten and slacken them. But everybody has the capacity to cover an extremely wide Pitch range; and the reasons why a person has a particularly high or low voice are primarily psychological.

We tend to raise the Pitch of the voice in joy and excitement and

49

many people with high voices like to reside in the realm of pleasure. But the high voice may also serve as a way of avoiding the sorrowful and sombre emotions associated with deeper notes.

Like sounds above a certain Loudness threshold, sounds produced by extremely high frequencies can be penetrating and destructive. High sounds are usually sensed as being sharp and can be experienced as piercing objects. Some people develop high voices in order to feel that they have the power to penetrate obstacles, cut through the opposition and forge the way ahead. Other people have extreme difficulty in accessing the high voice because the sense of power which the high voice evokes causes feelings of shame. For those who suffer from a depleted sense of self-worth, accessing the high voice can be extremely empowering. Reaching the high voice can feel as though we have reached new personal heights and achieved a heightened sense of awareness.

High sounds are experienced as being high in space and during a healing vocal journey the vocalist will often reach up with the body as though plucking notes from the air. High sounds instigate feelings of elation and flightiness, and for those people who seek to release themselves from the depressive monotony of the earth, making high sounds can be extremely liberating. But for those whose tendency is to be ungrounded and unearthed, high sounds can be disorientating and unsettling.

At the other end of the pitch scale is the low voice, which in opera is called bass. This 'bass' voice often expresses the 'base' aspects of our soul which has two dimensions. Firstly, our base is our bedrock, our foundations and the ground upon which our character stands. To access the low voice therefore gives us a sense of deep-rootedness, strength and support. But base also means crude, unrefined, flagrant, obscene and coarse; and vocalizing with the low voice enables us to express a certain primeval core of sensation. For those whose healing requires a redeeming of animal instincts and primal passions, the low voice can be very liberating. The low voice feels as though it emerges from deep in the body and making bass sounds can stimulate the sexual organs and stir erotic energy. Many people avoid low sounds as a way of evading their sexuality.

The deep voice is experienced as being low in space and when we vocalize with a bass voice it feels as if we are descending into the depths physically and emotionally. The low voice can cause us to feel down in the dumps, in the pits, in the doldrums and depressed. Many people have deep voices because their soul resides in the depths of depression; whilst others avoid low sounds so they do not have to confront the morose and depressive aspects of themselves. Our voice descends in sorrow and rises in joy; and many people develop low voices because they have become overwhelmed with sorrow and forgotten the magic of joy.

The low voice sounds as though it emerges from the depths and is therefore associated with depth of integrity, depth of meaning and authority. The high voice can therefore be misread as superficial and lacking in psychological depth. Some people develop low voices in order to preserve a sense of psychological depth while others develop high voices in order to avoid the responsibility which comes from speaking from the depths.

Claiming the healing voice means recalling the complete spectrum of this ingredient from the extreme heights to the very depths of the Pitch range and using this spectrum to give voice to the highs and lows of the heart and soul.

Ingredient three – pitch fluctuation

When we vocalize, the speed with which the vocal cords vibrate does not remain constant but wavers to some degree. Even if we attempt to sing a single note for a prolonged period of time, for example middle C, the vocal cords will not sustain their opening and closing at an exact and constant 256 times per second. There will be some fluctuation as the vocal cords vibrate a little faster and a little slower in a given

Voice Movement Therapy Exercise

Developing Pitch

Now you have explored the spectrum of Loudness, return to a note in the middle of your Pitch range and begin ascending and descending in Pitch with moderate Loudness. When you reach what feels like the top of your Pitch range, try adjusting the Loudness to see if this helps you go higher than you have before. Do the same thing when you reach what feels like the bottom of your Pitch range. When you have found the level of Loudness which enables you to extend the ends of your Pitch range, practise going a little higher and a little lower than you would normally so that in time you extend the range of pitches available to you.

unit of time. In Western singing, if the fluctuation is too great, for example fluctuating between 236 and 276 times per second, then the note will sound wobbly and the voice will be judged to be out of tune, particularly if the fluctuation is very slow. But if the fluctuation is minimal – for example between 246 and 266 times per second – and the fluctuation occurs very quickly, then the note will have a quality known as vibrato and the voice will be judged to be classically beautiful. Yet both the revered vibrato and the despised wavering are produced by the same effect. This effect is called Pitch Fluctuation.

In many forms of singing the voice is free to fluctuate spontaneously without falling prey to extreme judgements regarding its musical viability. Many of these singing styles originate in the extension of the speaking voice and capitalize on the fact that the speaking voice fluctuates freely in people from all cultures without regard to musical correctness. To draw upon the healing power of the voice we have to suspend our Western judgements and allow the voice to fluctuate freely, just as the soul fluctuates in its wheel of passions.

The third ingredient of the human voice is therefore Pitch Fluctuation, which is perceived as being fast or slow, great or small.

The healing power of pitch fluctuation

In daily life, Pitch Fluctuation occurs to our voice when we are extremely anxious or nervous; and often the quivering can tingle through the muscles of our whole body. Vocalizing with Pitch Fluctuation can instil feelings of uncertainty, creating the sensation of having an insecure and unstable personality; and those who have a lot of Pitch Fluctuation in their voice are often of a nervous and insecure disposition. For those whose healing journey is concerned with replacing an insecure persona with confidence and ease, substituting Pitch Fluctuation with constant tones is extremely assuring. On the other hand, those whose voices lack Pitch Fluctuation may be holding fast to their security and avoiding the vulnerable and uncertain parts of themselves. For people whose healing requires old patterns to be shaken up and fixed habits to be dislodged, vocalizing with Pitch Fluctuation can provide the earthquake out of which fresh perspectives can grow.

Pitch Fluctuation often occurs when we are excited and for those who have lost the elated and tumultuous part of the soul, vocalizing with Pitch Fluctuation can serve to arouse the spirit. But, Pitch Fluctuation also occurs when we are afraid; and vocalizing with it can evoke feelings of panic and fright. For those whose lives are limited by

[*Voice Movement Therapy Exercise*

Developing Pitch Fluctuation

Now you have a wide Pitch range that you can sing with varying degrees of Loudness, try to vocalize this range with Pitch Fluctuation. Firstly, sing your Pitch range with a very fast Fluctuation, like a classical vibrato. Then, sing the range again with a slower Pitch Fluctuation. As you do this, vary the level of Loudness and continue seeking to go higher and lower than you have before, allowing yourself to celebrate having three vocal ingredients to play with.]

fear, it is extremely healing to replace Pitch Fluctuation with constant notes. But for those who want to taste fear again in order to reclaim the sense of forces greater than themselves, vocalizing with Pitch Fluctuation can serve to unnerve the complacent spirit and fill the soul with awe and respect for the unknown.

Drawing upon the healing voice means holding fast to the constancy of tones as well as allowing those tones to fluctuate so that the complete spectrum of the self can be expressed in sound.

Ingredient four – register

If you sing the lowest note in your Pitch range and rise one note at a time up to the highest, you will notice that somewhere in the middle there is a transitional point where a particular change occurs to the quality of the voice. The upper notes will probably seem to have a brighter quality while the lower notes will sound darker. The point where this change occurs is called the Register break. The two main Registers are Modal and Falsetto. The lower range of notes which sound darker are in Modal Register and the upper range of notes which sound brighter are in Falsetto Register. In the Western classical tradition, a female Falsetto voice is called 'head Register' and her Modal voice is called 'chest Register'. These terms originate in the antiquated idea that Falsetto Register generates more vibration in the head whilst the Modal Register resonates more in the chest; but there is no scientific evidence for this. The term Falsetto comes from the Latin for 'false' and calling this quality of voice 'Falsetto Register' in a male voice and 'head Register' in a female voice implies that it is false for a man but not for a women to sing with this quality. Indeed, the association between Falsetto and femininity is exaggerated in the pastiche cabaret and pantomime when men use the Falsetto Register to impersonate the speaking voice of a woman. This is of course unfounded because neither women nor men speak in Falsetto, but in Modal. But both men and women do use Falsetto in their talking voice at times of extreme emotion, such as when we sob or laugh.

In opera, singers are prohibited from exposing the change of Register and each singer must use one or the other. The male voices are always sung in Modal – with the exception of the male counter tenor – while Falsetto is reserved for women. In training voices for the classical stage, singers are taught a technique called 'blending', where the two registers are mixed together to form one quality and any noticeable change of register during singing is eradicated. But outside of European classical music, in Western contemporary singing and non-Western indigenous styles, both Registers are used freely by men and women and are not associated with masculinity or femininity. The Register break is particularly exaggerated in the yodelling style of singing often associated with the indigenous music of the Swiss Alps and amongst the North America 'singing cowboys' such as Jimmie Rodgers, Eddy Arnold and Tennessee Ernie Ford. Some of these men sing from the range of an operatic bass up to the heights associated with the soprano. Elvis Presley and Roy Orbison also moved fluidly between Modal and Falsetto. There have also been a number of contemporary Western male singers who sing exclusively in the Falsetto Register, such as the Bee Gees and Jimmy Somerville; and there are female singers who make a point of singing exclusively in Modal Register such as Tracy Chapman.

Although the higher Pitch range of a voice is usually sung in Falsetto and the lower Pitch range in Modal, Register is not directly related to Pitch because with practice you can sing a range of notes in Modal and then sing the same range notes again in Falsetto.

Because the deliberate exposure of the Register break is not allowed in opera, trainees of classical singing learn a technique called blending. This involves ascending and descending the Pitch range, gradually blending the qualities of Falsetto and Modal into a single quality known as a 'blended Register' so that the break is eradicated. However, this also eradicates the special emotional magnetism of the Register break. To reclaim the full power of the voice, it is necessary to develop both the Modal and Falsetto Registers and allow the voice to move between the two as the mood requires.

The fourth ingredient of the voice is therefore Register which is perceived as being either Modal, Falsetto or blended.

The healing power of register

A common term for a change in Register is a 'break' and indeed as the voice passes from Modal to Falsetto or vice versa it can feel as though something is breaking. Some people have a constant Register break in their daily voice; and often this reveals a deep part of the self which has been broken and has not healed. Our voice breaks naturally when we are breaking down with emotion; and deep crying is often character- ized by a sobbing back and forth between the two Registers. But the same Register break often occurs when we laugh fully and without restraint. Some people never allow the Registers to change, even when they laugh or cry, as a way of avoiding contact with genuine emotion. For those people whose healing is concerned with finding access to tumultuous emotions and reactivating the passions of the heart, the Register break can be extremely liberating. On the other hand, for those who experience a constant 'breaking' of emotion, replacing the Register break with a blended constant quality can be very stabilizing and strengthening.

In the Western world Falsetto is associated more with femininity and Modal with masculinity, and use of the opposite registers can have a healing power when it comes to sexuality. When a man accesses pure Falsetto and a woman accesses pure Modal, sexual stereo- types can be overcome and a more holistic sense of gender can be invigorated.

Because the Falsetto Register is the quality which characterizes a child's voice, accessing the Falsetto can animate the inner child; and for those who have lost the spirit of youth, this can be very healing.

Voice Movement Therapy Exercise

Developing Register

Start singing at the bottom of your Pitch range and ascend one note at a time. Listen for the two notes where the voice changes from Modal to Falsetto Register. Now refind those notes and sing them over and over, vocalizing on a yodel. Then, having acquired the art of the Register break, practise yodelling in other parts of your Pitch range, allowing yourself to create improvised melodies which use Modal and Falsetto. Finally, sing a range of notes in Modal and then practise singing the same range of notes in Falsetto.

Conversely, for those whose lives are under the constant spell of regression and whose healing journey seeks for an opportunity to mature, the Modal voice can be very grounding.

Using the healing voice means allowing the voice to break out of one Register into another so that we may break out of the fixity of a rigid self and express our capacity for change and growth.

Ingredient five – harmonic timbre

The section of the voice tube which runs from the lips to the larynx can change its length and its diameter; and because of the laws of acoustics, the same note produced by the vibration of the vocal cords will resonate with a very different quality if the voice tube is short and narrow to the quality produced when the voice tube is lengthened and dilated.

To understand this, imagine three basic tubes, closed at the bottom but open at the top, constructed to different diameters and different lengths. The first is short and narrow; the second is relatively longer and wider; and the third is much longer and more dilated again. Imagine that we hold a tuning fork vibrating at 256 times per second –

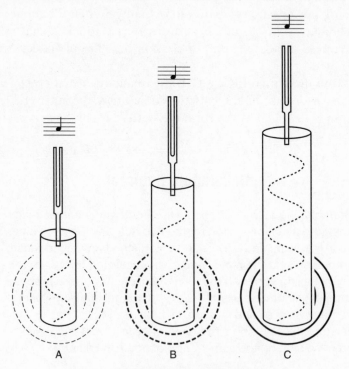

Figure 4 **Understanding harmonic timbre**

which produces middle C – over the top of each tube in turn and listen to the sound of the note echoing or resonating inside the tubes (*see* figure 4). In moving from listening to the sound inside the first tube to the same note echoing or resonating in the second and then the third, we would hear a change of timbre. Perhaps the sound in the first tube would sound 'bright', 'twangy', 'shiny' and 'shimmery'; perhaps the sound resonating in the second tube, by comparison, would sound 'thicker', more 'solemn' or 'fruitier'; and perhaps the sound resonating in the third tube would sound 'full', 'moaning', 'rounded' and 'dark'. Probably, the first tube would sound more comparable to a flute, the second tube would sound more comparable to the clarinet, whilst the sound produced by the third tube would sound more akin to the saxophone; they would all however produce the note C.

With regard to voice production, both the length and the diameter of the voice tube can alter. The diameter of the voice tube can increase by opening the mouth and stretching the throat; and the length of the voice tube can increase by lowering the larynx in the neck. The tube can therefore assume three different configurations comparable to the three shapes as the three crude tubes. The first is called Flute Configuration, whereby the larynx is high in the neck and the tube is quite narrow, such as when we blow a kiss or whistle (*see* figure 5). The second is called Clarinet Configuration, whereby the larynx is positioned in the middle of the neck and the tube is more dilated, such as when we steam up a pair of glasses (*see* figure 6). The third is called Saxophone Configuration, whereby the larynx is fully descended in the neck and the tube is dilated to its maximum, such as when we yawn (*see* figure 7).

If the vibration of the vocal cords is maintained at a constant vibratory frequency, say at 256 times per second, producing middle C, whilst the vocal tract moves from Flute Configuration through Clarinet Configuration to Saxophone Configuration, the effect will be to sing the same note with three very distinct timbres, comparable to that achieved when playing the note C on a tuning fork held above the three separate crude tubes imagined earlier. In Voice Movement Therapy, we give the vocal colour produced by a short narrow voice tube the instrumental name Flute Timbre; we name the vocal colour produced by a medium length and diameter tube Clarinet Timbre; and we call the vocal colour produced by a fully lengthened and dilated voice tube Saxophone Timbre.

The fifth ingredient of the human voice is therefore Harmonic Timbre which can be Flute, Clarinet or Saxophone, depending on the configuration of the voice tube.

Figure 5 **Flute Configuration**

The healing power of harmonic timbre

The breath emerging from the tube when it is in Flute Configuration is cold – it is the shape we make with our mouth when we want to cool down hot food by blowing air from the mouth. The sound of the Flute Timbre can also feel cool, passionless, stoic and frosty. Furthermore, because the Flute Configuration tube is so narrow, it does not discharge a great deal of acoustic or emotional material and can sound very reserved and conservative. For those whose healing journey is directed towards learning to preserve more energy and more privacy, such as those who have been depleted and exhausted by their tendency to give too much of themselves, vocalizing in Flute Timbre can be

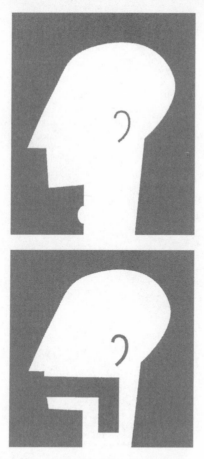

Figure 6 **Clarinet Configuration**

very helpful. But for those seeking to release more of their soul into the world, it is necessary to expand the dimensions of the voice tube. In singing, the Flute Timbre is heard at its most constant in Christian plainsong, such as the Gregorian chant.

Whilst the Flute Configuration tends to release a minimum amount of breath and sound, the Saxophone Configuration releases the entire flood and holds very little back. For those who are seeking to release themselves from the stifling confines of a reserved and retained psyche, vocalizing in Saxophone Timbre can be extremely transforming. Common reasons for expanding the throat to the dimensions of the Saxophone Configuration are to belch or vomit. Therefore, vocalizing with the Saxophone Timbre can feel as though we are going to bring things up from the stomach. It is, in fact, very rare for someone to

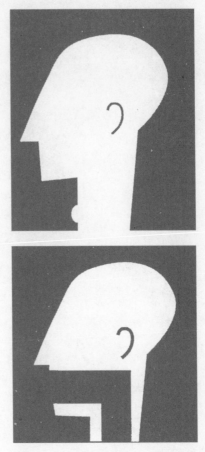

Figure 7 **Saxophone Configuration**

actually vomit when vocalizing in Saxophone Timbre; however, it is common for people to initially experience the Saxophone Timbre as 'sick' and ugly. Although this can be terrifying, it is also very liberating for those whose healing is connected to being released from the pressure of having to be beautiful, sweet and correct.

Another reason for expanding the voice tube dimensions to the maximum is to cry; and vocalizing with the Saxophone Timbre often induces sobbing, which can be very liberating for those who have become separated from their sorrows. On the other hand, for those who seek to be healed from feeling overwhelmed with the water of their sadness, it is helpful to narrow the voice tube to clarinet or flute. In singing, the Saxophone Timbre is often heard in gospel and jazz; Cleo Laine and Nina Simone, for example, both use fully expanded

Voice Movement Therapy Exercise

Developing Harmonic Timbre

Stand comfortably and breathe in and out through your mouth. Narrow the voice tube to Flute Configuration by whistling or blowing cool air as though to lower the temperature of hot food (*see* figure 8). Imagine that the voice tube is very narrow and that it extends from the lips down to the indent between the clavicles at the top of the breastbone. Now begin to vocalize, singing up and down your Pitch range

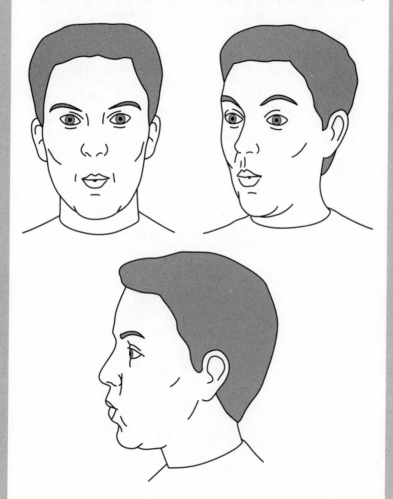

Figure 8 **The facial expression of Flute Configuration**

Voice Movement Therapy Exercise

with varying degrees of Loudness in Modal and Falsetto Register, listening to the Flute Timbre of the voice.

Now expand the dimensions of the voice tube to Clarinet Configuration, opening the mouth and expanding the throat. Imagine that you are steaming up a window or a pair of spectacles and feel how the expired breath is now warm (*see* figure 9). Imagine that the tube is wide and that it extends from the lips down to the centre of the torso at the bottom of the breastbone. Now begin to vocalize, singing up and down your Pitch range with varying degrees of Loudness in Modal and Falsetto Register, listening to the Clarinet Timbre of the voice.

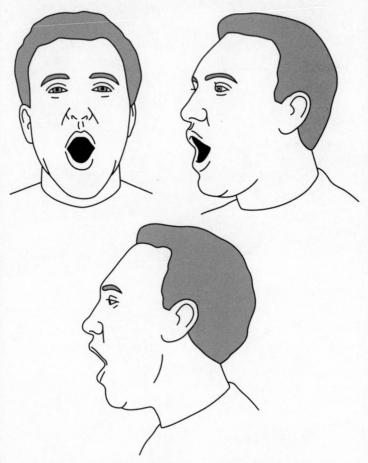

Figure 9 **The facial expression of Clarinet Configuration**

Voice Movement Therapy Exercise

Now expand the voice tube to its maximum dimensions, dilating mouth and throat as though yawning and imagine that the tube extends from the lips all the way down into the belly (*see* figure 10). Now begin to vocalize, singing up and down your Pitch range with varying degrees of Loudness in Modal and Falsetto Register, listening to the Saxophone Timbre of the voice.

Now, take a melody and sing it first in Flute Timbre then with Clarinet Timbre and then with Saxophone Timbre but keeping all the other vocal ingredients constant so that you can hear specifically the three distinct Harmonic Timbres.

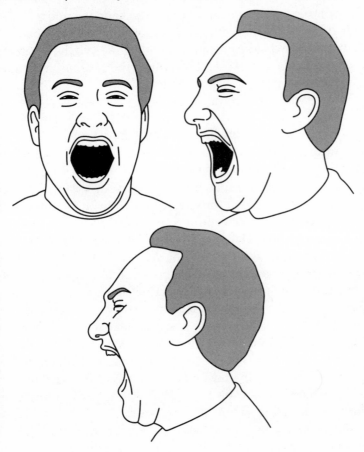

Figure 10 **The facial expression of Saxophone Configuration**

voice tube configurations.

Between Flute and Saxophone is the Clarinet Timbre, which is emblematic of the middle ground. It can narrow to Flute or it can expand to Saxophone. For those seeking to increase their choices and dexterity, the Clarinet Configuration is a grail worth pursuing, for it is a platform from which all else is possible.

In Voice Movement Therapy, being able to expand the voice tube dimensions is the single most important part of the physical work. For the expanded tube enables all the other vocal ingredients to be reverberated, amplified and enhanced. Expanding the tube therefore enables people to make the most of themselves, to reveal themselves in all their colours. However, dealing with all the psychological inhibitions which prevent the tube from expanding and the soul from being amplified constitutes one of the most important areas of psychological work. Expanding the tube means expanding the self; thus it sits at the core of the healing process. Reclaiming the healing voice means allowing the voice tube to expand to its maximum so that we may be reverberated without restraint.

Ingredient six – nasality

As the air carries the sound up from the larynx, not all of it passes through the mouth and exits at the lips; some also passes up above the roof of the mouth and through the nasal passages, exiting at the nose. Sound that passes through this tube resonates with a quality usually referred to as nasal. In Voice Movement Therapy, we give this nasal quality the instrumental name Violin which mixes in with the Flute, Clarinet or Saxophone Timbre of the voice.

The more air that passes through the nasal passages, the more Nasality or Violin the sound of the voice will have; and the quantity of air passing through the passages is controlled by a flap of tissue known as the soft palate. This trap door hangs at the back of the throat and can open and close by degrees. If it is completely closed, then the voice has no Violin and lacks Nasality. If it is completely open, then the voice has a lot of Violin and sounds very nasal. Between these two extremes a whole spectrum is possible, like adding or subtracting violins from the string section of an orchestra.

Violin is the quality of voice that Western children use when they impersonate a Chinese or Japanese person; and though this is a social stereotype, Nasality is in fact a tonal colour inherent in a lot of indigenous Oriental singing and can be heard in the voices of the Cantonese Opera, the Shanghai Opera and those of the Hát Chéo

Folk Theatre of Vietnam. There have also been a number of Western contemporary singers whose voices are infused with a lot of Violin, such as Billie Holiday, Marlene Dietrich, Neil Young and the early work of Bob Dylan.

The sixth ingredient of the voice is therefore Nasality or Violin which is perceived on a spectrum from minimum to maximum.

The healing power of nasality

Violin is the quality of voice which people automatically use when impersonating a baby and a very old person. Violin therefore carries with it issues connected to age. People who complain that their voice is too childlike usually have a lot of Violin in their voice and by learning to decrease nasal resonance they can experience a new self image, replacing naïvety with maturity.

It is very common for actors to use Nasality when playing someone wicked and it is our natural tendency to use Violin when we are expressing spite and vindictiveness. For those seeking to get in touch with their malice and animosity, vocalizing with Violin can be very provocative.

Nasality is used a lot more in the speaking voice than in most Western singing styles. In fact, there are certain vowels in the English

Voice Movement Therapy Exercise

Developing Nasality

Take a note in the middle of your Pitch range and sing it with moderate Loudness without Pitch Fluctuation in Modal Register and Clarinet Timbre. Now, as you sing the note, add Violin by making the sound more nasal. Then practise singing this note with a spectrum of Violin from minimum to maximum.

Now sing another note with moderate Loudness, without Pitch Fluctuation and in Clarinet Timbre but in Falsetto Register and again practise increasing and decreasing the amount of Violin.

When you have acquired control of Nasality, begin experimenting with different combinations of the other vocal ingredients as you play with the addition and subtraction of Violin.

language, such as 'i' as in 'sit', which cannot be adequately communicated without increasing Nasality – which is why they are called 'nasal vowels'. In indigenous cultures where the singing style has evolved from speaking and calling, there is often a lot more Violin in the voice. Reclaiming the healing voice means reconnecting to a world voice which can encapsulate the sounds of all nations and all cultures. Accessing Violin is therefore a key to sonically empathizing with the voices of other lands and can help us get in touch with our multicultural and transpersonal self.

Acoustically, Violin brings to the voice a certain hardness and density, enabling the voice to be projected over greater distances and to be heard above other noise. This is another reason why indigenous singing styles which have originated in the open air and where people had to sing to each other over large distances tend to have a lot of Violin in the voice. For those who wish to acquire the ability to project their voice, vocalizing with Violin is extremely supportive and brings strength and solidity to the sound.

Reclaiming the healing voice means drawing on the complete spectrum of Nasality in the voice, allowing the colourful shades of our vocal canvas to mirror the prism of the soul.

Ingredient seven – free air

When the vocal cords vibrate, they push together momentarily many times per second. But if, during their moment of contact, they do not push tightly together, then breath seeps through the crack. When this happens, the sound of the voice is very breathy. In Voice Movement Therapy such a breathy quality in the tonal colour of a voice is called Free Air. The more loosely the vocal cords push together, the more Free Air the voice will have.

During the 1950s, Julie London elevated the Free Air voice to new heights with her rendition of 'Cry Me A River', and there are a number of singers in more recent Western contemporary music whose voices have a lot of Free Air, such as Art Garfunkel.

The seventh ingredient of the human voice is therefore Free Air which is generally referred to as the 'breathiness' of a voice and is perceived on a spectrum from minimum to maximum.

The healing power of free air

Increasing Free Air is something which many people do when expressing empathy, gentility and receptivity, whilst voices without any Free Air usually sound firm. For those people seeking to melt their hard exterior and access their underlying sensitivity, vocalizing with maximum Free Air is ideal. But for those who tend to leave themselves without guard and protection, vocalizing with minimum Free Air can create a greater sense of strength and resilience.

A voice rich in Free Air is often associated with sexuality; and sexuality is always latently present in the act of singing. The art of singing is, in essence, founded upon the ability to stimulate and arouse the listener with the sumptuous use of the mouth. Some singers have exaggerated the sensual aspect to singing and often use Free Air to eroticize the tonal colour of their voice. Marilyn Monroe was probably the first to epitomize this style. For those seeking to uncover their buried sexuality, vocalizing with Free Air can be extremely liberating, unleashing the libido in sound.

We also tend to fill the voice with Free Air when we are exasperated and perplexed; and vocalizing with Free Air can tap into these feelings.

Vocalizing with Free Air is exhausting because the sound absorbs so much breath that you have to replenish the air in the lungs frequently, only to lose it all again in the next sound. This can create a feeling of futility and of 'not getting anywhere'. For people with this experience, as well as for those who feel that they lack reserves and who need to lessen their tendency to over-expand, decreasing the amount of Free Air can be very healing. But for those who feel the tension and pressure of keeping their spirit contained, increasing the amount of Free Air in the voice can feel extremely releasing.

Reclaiming the healing voice means taking hold of the ability to

Voice Movement Therapy Exercise

Developing Free Air

Sing an improvised melody in a voice with moderate Loudness. Now repeat the singing but this time sing it as though you are vocalizing on a whisper. As you sing, make the sound as breathy as you can, filling the voice with Free Air. Now, decrease the amount of Free Air so that the voice is moderately breathy. Finally, remove the Free Air completely and sing with a voice that is firm and solid. Finally, practise combining varying amounts of Free Air with all the other vocal ingredients.

vary the amount of Free Air in the voice, as our sentiments and intentions require.

Ingredient eight – attack

The pressure of the breath travelling up from the lungs determines the force with which the vocal cords contact each other during vibration which in turn determines the Loudness of the voice. However, the vocal cords also have the capacity to hit into each other under the power of their own neuromuscular connections. This means that they can increase or decrease the force of contact. This extra dimension to vocal cord vibration is called Attack. Increased Attack does not make the voice louder but it gives it a certain stress.

The eighth ingredient of the human voice is therefore Attack which gives a voice its stress and is perceived on a spectrum from lesser to greater.

The healing power of attack

Vocal Attack is used when we want to attack our subject with a strength of opinion and certainty and those whose voices are naturally abundant with this quality are often quite strong-minded and strong-willed individuals. We often use increased Attack when we are driving our point home with the punctilious and percussive points of our argument. Vocal Attack is often used when we are certain of ourselves; and those people with a lot of Attack in their voices are often those with a high sense of self-esteem and sometimes self-righteousness. For those people who have succumbed to this mask at the expense of their vulnerable and uncertain self, decreasing Attack can uncover a tone of greater humility.

Those whose voices lack Attack are often dealing with reticence and self-doubt, lacking the necessary belief in themselves with which to attack the world with their voice. For those with a tendency to acquiesce and relinquish their beliefs when intimidated or opposed, vocalizing with Attack can help to muster a new adversarial spirit and consolidate the ability to hold ground.

Because Attack tends to create a percussive dimension, people who naturally use this quality are usually those who think in a linear direction and feel at ease with logic and lists of reasons for and against the decision at hand. Those who lack this quality in their voice, on the other hand, are generally those more at ease with non-linear intuitive thought which meanders and explores issues elliptically. Attack is the rhythmic component to the voice and, for those whose expressions are

Voice Movement Therapy Exercise

Developing Attack

To develop increased Attack, take a series of vowels
preceded by an 'H' and say them quickly and percussively
on the expired breath as though you are releasing a series of
bullets: Ha, Hi, Ho, He. Then, sustain the strength of the
Attack through an extended note on these sounds:
Haaaaaaaa, Hiiiiiiii, Hoooooooo, Heeeeeeee.

full of flow but who have lost a sense of tempo in their lives, vocalizing
with Attack can be very grounding. On the other hand, those whose
voices have been sequestered by the overbearing demands of time can
experience a healing liberation by replacing Attack with the soft edges
of a gentle tonal colour in their voice.

Reclaiming the healing voice means being able to vary the degree
of Attack in the voice and use the complete spectrum at will.

Ingredient nine – disruption

Sometimes, the two vocal cords do not meet so as to create a flush,
smooth edge but instead crash together unevenly with corrugated
edges, rubbing into each other and creating friction. When this
happens the tonal colour of the voice becomes rough and the Pitch
becomes discontinuous. In Voice Movement Therapy such a voice is
described as possessing Disruption. Disrupted sounds also arise when
other tissue structures of the larynx vibrate or come into contact with
the vocal cords.

Disruption is a key component of many non-Western indigenous
singing styles, such as the chanting of Tibetan monks and the rough
calling of flamenco deep song. However, singers of these traditions
have great difficulty in producing any other kind of non-disrupted
sound because constant friction between the vocal cords causes
damage to their constituting tissue. There are also many people in the
tradition of Western contemporary music who have used Disruption
such as Janis Joplin, Louis Armstrong, Rod Stewart, Tom Waits,
Bonnie Tyler and Tina Turner; and some of these people have also
suffered vocal damage. However there are ways of producing a
disrupted voice which protect the cords from damage, but these

techniques need to be learned from someone first hand.

The ninth ingredient of the human voice is therefore Disruption and is perceived on a spectrum from mild to severe.

The healing power of disruption

We tend to use disruption when we are extremely angry and when we are scolding someone with a warning; and those with naturally disrupted voices are often host to a backlog of rage. However, the voice also disrupts when we are emotionally disrupted and many people with such voices have been shattered by intense and overwhelming experiences. Conversely, those people who have difficulty vocalizing with Disruption are often avoiding both their anger and the broken, disrupted and shattered part of themselves. People who cannot access their disrupted voices tend to be stoic and highly attached to the idea of themselves as able and well balanced. For such people, the sound of Disruption is too extreme and too threatening, for it promises to over-

Voice Movement Therapy Exercise

Developing Disruption

You should not practise Disruption for longer than a few minutes unless you have been taught a technique by a proficient master or mistress first hand. The safest way to get a sense of Disruption is to vocalize very quietly in the middle of your Pitch range in Modal Register with very little Attack and in Saxophone Timbre.

Begin vocalizing on a single note and then start to gently groan as though simmering with fury. As your voice becomes disrupted, travel up and down the lower part of your Pitch range and improvise a melody.

turn the polished persona by sprinkling grit across the smooth surface of the vocal mask. For those seeking to unearth their anger or disturb the perfect grace of their clean-cut persona, accessing Disruption can be radically transformative.

Ingredient ten – articulation

When we are babies we use the complete palette of articulate shapes available to us as we sculpt vocal sounds with the lips, jaw and tongue.

But when we learn the mother tongue we abandon this range for the narrow spectrum of our spoken language. Only in extreme circumstances, such as speaking in tongues during spiritual ritual or speaking in psychic disarray during mental illness, do we reclaim this spectrum of Articulation.

The two units of Articulation that are present in all tongues are vowels and consonants. Vowels are open sounds made from a continuous air flow. Consonants are plosive sounds made by interrupting the air flow. In Voice Movement Therapy, Articulation does not refer just to the vowels and consonants of a single recognizable linguistic code; it refers to the complete range of articulated structures which can be created by the human vocal instrument. To reclaim the healing voice means returning to the complete palette of sculpted sounds – in effect it means singing in all tongues.

The tenth ingredient of the human voice is therefore Articulation which is the sculpting of the vocal sound into vowels and consonants with mouth, lips, tongue and jaw.

The healing power of articulation

In the early stages of accessing the complete range of the voice, any form of articulation can be restricting, causing the throat to tighten and the voice tube to narrow in preparation for words. But, Articulation is also a very liberating ingredient of the human voice because it

Voice Movement Therapy Exercise

Developing Articulation

Begin by calling from the heart. Let your voice ascend and descend in Pitch and allow the ingredients of the voice to combine spontaneously. Then begin to articulate familiar word units: Ta, Go, Sha, Be. As you call from the heart, start to allow yourself to give shape to word units that are less familiar to you: Ach, Unf, Tfi, Yin. Imagine that you are touring the world's languages, singing excerpts from every tongue that ever was. As you sing more imagine that you are touring the Occident and the Orient, the northern and the southern hemispheres of the globe and give voice to the lands which you discover.

provides a sense of giving a precise shape to the feeling carried by the voice. For those who find the spoken language of their mother tongue an unfriendly means of communication, singing in a multitude of spontaneous tongues provides a deep level of psychological release as though a new and perfect language has been uncovered.

The complete palette

These ten ingredients make up the palette of tonal colours that can be heard woven into the fabric of every human voice. This system of ingredients is an inspiring window through which to listen to the voices of the world; and they provide a framework within which you can analyse and understand what you hear. The system also provides a template for the development of your own voice; and I have pro-vided a comprehensive demonstration of all the vocal ingredients in the singing and speaking voice on my audio course *The Singing Cure*.

To recap, the ten ingredients which make up the human voice are:

Ingredient One – Loudness, perceived on a spectrum from loud to quiet.

Ingredient two – Pitch, perceived on a spectrum from low to high.

Ingredient three – Pitch Fluctuation, perceived as being fast or slow, great or small.

Ingredient four – Register, perceived as either Modal, Falsetto or blended.

Ingredient five – Harmonic Timbre, which can be Flute, Clarinet or Saxophone.

Ingredient six – Nasality or Violin, perceived on a spectrum from minimum to maximum.

Ingredient seven – Free Air, perceived on a spectrum from minimum to maximum.

Ingredient eight – Attack, perceived on a spectrum from lesser to greater.

Ingredient nine – Disruption, perceived on a spectrum from mild to severe.

Ingredient ten – Articulation, perceived as a sculpting of the voice into vowels and consonants.

Healing and damage

Although Disruption is one of the most common causes for people to damage their voice, in fact any misguided voice production technique can cause impairment to the vocal instrument. Damaged voices fall into two categories: organic and functional. Organic voice disorders are those where the actual tissue and flesh of the vocal apparatus becomes deformed or diseased. These disorders include laryngitis, growths on the vocal cords or a tumour in the larynx. Functional voice disorders, meanwhile, are conditions which inhibit and restrict the healthy and optimal use of the voice without causing physical damage. These problems usually occur as a result of misusing the voice and they are very common. Because these functional problems don't make themselves known during a medical examination, people with a functional voice problem often go through life without attracting very much understanding or help and have to live with feelings of despair and a constant dissatisfaction with their voice. Such voices are often intermittently lost and without warning they can become crackly or husky, breathy or squeaky; they can become fixed in a narrow range of just a few notes, or become faint and barely audible, or feel completely blocked and constrained; and a person with a functional voice problem can be left with a sore throat every time they use their voice to any extent.

To work as a healing practitioner through the medium of voice requires an informed knowledge of the way the voice functions as a physical and biological instrument. I have worked with many people whose voices have been abused by training techniques and therapeutic processes which have not been properly grounded in a respect for basic physiological and mechanical principles. This is why the accredited professional training course in Voice Movement Therapy includes a careful study of the vocal mechanism. But to facilitate healing through the voice also requires an intimate sensitivity to the psychological aspects of vocal expression; and this is why trainee Voice Movement Therapists spend so much time investigating the relationship between sound and psyche. For I have also worked with many whose voices have been abused by insubstantial respect for the emotional component of vocal expression.

An enormous proportion of voice problems, organic and functional, originate in an emotional or psychological issue. I have worked with people whose voices have been reduced to a whisper as a result of rape or sexual abuse; people whose voices are cramped and strained because underneath there lies a pool of unexpressed grief, rage or sorrow; and people who have degenerative conditions like multiple sclerosis and common conditions like asthma. But with all cases I am working with their heart and soul just as much as I am working with their voice. For a crackly voice may reveal a crack in the heart; a breathy voice may reveal an exasperated soul; a quiet voice may be the voice of someone who has been quietened down; a voice which cannot ascend in Pitch may be the voice of someone terrified of losing touch with the ground; a voice with a part of the range missing may be trying to show a part of the self that has been lost; a voice that has lost its ability to play and dance with spontaneity is often a sign of a soul which has lost the ability to make itself known to the world without apology or apprehension. All of our feelings and thoughts, our moods and instincts are revealed in the sound of the voice and these are intensified and magnified through the process of singing. In the cradle before we learned language and acquired the fatal disease of self-consciousness, we knew this and we sang for our supper hour in and hour out. Now, many people have lost that ability, the ability to cry out, call out, sing out. This is where the real damage is, the damage to our birth right, the damage to our right to sound out, to sound the soul. But this damage can also impede the physical functioning of the vocal instrument; and to repair such damage therefore requires a true holism which addresses the psychics and the somatics of sound.

CHAPTER SIX

Finding Room to Breathe

*How our breath affects every sound we make and
why changing the way we breathe can enhance the
way we feel*

The way we breathe

There can be no voice without breath; and the way we breathe influences the way we sound. Even without the pitch generated by the vocal cords, the sound of our breath alone reveals the music of our moods: the huffs and puffs of fury, the gasps of bewilderment and surprise, the sudden and abrupt jets of achievement and accomplishment, the elongated draughts of depression and submission, the protracted sucks of expectation and the long blows of delight and relief. At times of severe trauma our breath becomes a tempest which rouses our terror and kindles our shock as we heave and pant, losing all semblance of calm. At times of exquisite tranquillity, our breath whispers the music of our equanimity and nonchalance.

To breathe deeply is to take in the spirit of the world and have it permeate the cells of body and soul. To breathe in shallow proportion is to guard against this spirit, leaving us half empty, half touched, half blessed and half fulfilled. So many among us take in only the bare essentials: a meagre cup of breath swallowed in haste and expelled with habitual depreciation. Some people breathe with such modesty and minority that it is as though they are embarrassed to drink up the stuff of life and loathe to release their inner essence into the world. Others restrict their breath because they feel they have no room to breathe; their lungs feel trapped and incarcerated and their life is on a leash. Some keep their breathing shallow and inconsequential because they have lived their life pacifying an aggressor, tranquillizing a volatile atmosphere and keeping the peace amidst an explosive terrain. They have learned to breathe cautiously as they tip-toe through the minefield of emotional mayhem.

I worked with one young woman called June whose breathing was so restricted you could not see any expansion and contraction in her torso during inspiration or expiration. She had been raised by parents who fought viciously and dangerously, often turning their violating attentions to June's younger brother and sister. June had been the adjudicator, stepping into the cross-fire of her parents' battle, calming the contention and rescuing her siblings from the ever-present threat of slapping hands and wicked words. June had learned to hold her breath. She was always on guard, always expectant, always aware that the slightest breeze could invoke the winds of change and raise the familiar typhoon of family violence.

Others breathe with self-effacing modesty because they are afraid of what might emerge if they burst forth with gusto and urgency. Breathing moves the stuff of life from the inside to the outside; breathing is revealing. To keep a secret we must not breathe a word and when news breaks, people get wind of things, as though knowledge is carried through the air. The best way not to be noticed is to hold your breath, as though through the cessation of breathing we become invisible. To breathe with an expansive fullness is to be seen. When we breathe in deeply we take up space, we use up air; and when we breathe out magnanimously we fill the space around us with the airborne fabric of our psyche.

Often, those who do not breathe to their full capacity harbour a reticence about coming forward and exerting their influence upon the world. They prefer to be unnoticed and would not presume to breathe more air than they need. They may feel that to take for themselves must surely mean they are taking away from someone else. It is difficult for them to imagine that there is enough air to go around, often because they have never received the bounty of inexhaustible love. Breath is full of love and when we make love our breathing scores the musical duet of our passion.

In many ancient stories, someone deceased or in a deep sleep is brought back to life when their lover breathes upon them. We speak of breathing fresh life into something and to revive our own life we must invoke the winds of change and imbibe the breath of life, filling our lungs with hope and compulsion. The Greek word *psyche* meaning 'soul' has the same root as the word *psychein* meaning 'to breathe'; and the Greek word *pneuma* meaning 'spirit' also means 'wind'. Furthermore, the Latin words *animus* meaning 'spirit' and *anima* meaning 'soul' come from the Greek *anemos*, which is another word for 'wind'. Similar connections exist in many other languages including German and Arabic and remind us that in many cultures the movement of the soul has been connected to the movement of the breath.

Just as the voice is composed of a set of ingredients which combine to produce the recipe for an array of vocal qualities, so the way we breathe is made up of different components which combine in various ways to produce distinct breathing patterns. A person's Breathing Pattern is the specific way in which the components of breathing combine to produce a habitual and familiar manner of inspiring and expiring. Because the way we breathe influences the way we sound and the way we feel, making changes to the Breathing Pattern can enable us to feel differently about ourselves and communicate the fullness of our being through our voice.

The components of the Breathing Pattern are:

Physical Expansion
Pressure
Frequency
Volume
Depth
Tube Configuration

Component one – physical expansion

The torso is a cylinder or large tube and to breathe to our maximum capacity we need to be able to increase the size of this tube, making room for the expansion of the lungs (*see* figure 11a). There are three ways of achieving this. Firstly, we can expand the walls of the cylinder outwards (*see* figure 11b). Secondly, we can lower the floor of the cylinder (*see* figure 11c). Thirdly, we can raise the roof of the cylinder (*see* figure 11d).

The expansion of the cylinder walls is achieved in the following way. The lungs are housed by a scaffolding of bones known as the rib

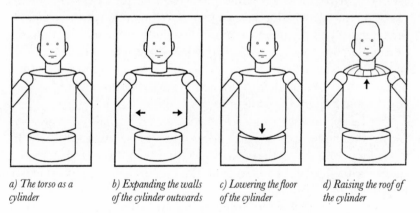

a) *The torso as a cylinder*

b) *Expanding the walls of the cylinder outwards*

c) *Lowering the floor of the cylinder*

d) *Raising the roof of the cylinder*

Figure 11 **Expansion of the torso 'cylinder'**

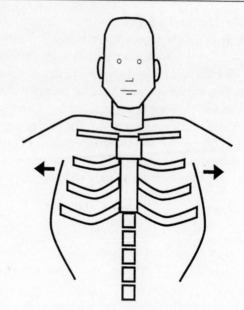

Figure 12 **Thoracic Expansion**

cage. Between the ribs there are muscles which, when contracted, lift the rib cage upwards and outwards, expanding the size of the torso and making room for the inflated lungs. When these muscles relax, the rib cage descends and recedes again. This is called Thoracic Expansion (*see* figure 12).

The lowering of the cylinder floor is achieved in the following way. Underneath the lungs is a long muscle called the diaphragm which stretches out from one side of the torso to the other and separates the thorax from the abdomen. This muscle is connected to a layer of tissue called the pleura which is in turn joined to the underneath surface of the lungs. When the diaphragm is relaxed it is shaped like an upside down salad bowl (*see* figure 13a). But when the diaphragm contracts, it is pulled downwards and flattened, pulling the bottom of the lungs down with it, causing them to expand from the bottom. This is called Abdominal Expansion (*see* figure 13b).

The raising of the cylinder roof is achieved in the following way. Across the upper back and shoulders there is a set of muscles which, when they contract, lift the collar bones, or clavicles, creating increased space for the lungs to expand from the top. This is called Clavicular Expansion (*see* figure 14).

Each of us breathes with more or less emphasis and movement in one of these three areas of expansion with inevitable psychological

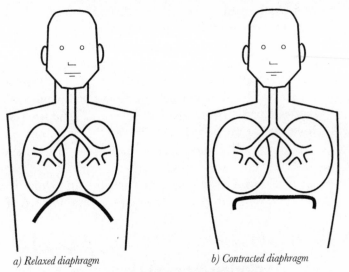

a) *Relaxed diaphragm*   b) *Contracted diaphragm*

Figure 13 **Abdominal Expansion**

consequences. For example, those who breathe with Thoracic Expansion at the expense of abdominal movement tend to be those who avoid the emotional depths of the belly and hold themselves upright. They also tend to be those whose energetic spectrum tends towards anxiety, as their breathing lacks the firm-rooted foundations of the

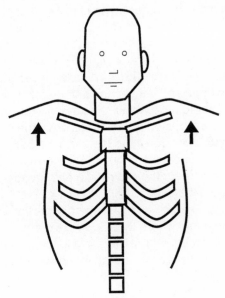

Figure 14 **Clavicular Expansion**

79

lower regions. On the other hand, those who breathe with Abdominal Expansion at the expense of thoracic movement tend to be those who 'sit in themselves'; and their energetic tendency is usually towards depression. Often they lack the verve and impulsiveness associated with the shallow breath of the upper chest, but they possess a calm depth of contemplation. Clavicular breathing, meanwhile, is usually used to a large extent during vigorous exercise, when extra air is needed. However, some people use this as their primary area of expansion and tend to be those whose bodies are tense and whose emotional reservoir is agitated and disturbed.

Clavicular Expansion is very often combined with a voice in Flute Configuration and is usually present in the Breathing Pattern of those

Voice Movement Therapy Exercise

Exploring Areas of Expansion

This is best explored with two people. The person whose Breathing Pattern is being explored stands comfortably and breathes in and out while the other person observes the areas of expansion. Placing one hand, palms down, on each of the partner's shoulders, the explorer senses the amount of movement in the area of Clavicular Expansion, feeling for the rise and fall of the shoulders. Then the explorer places a hand, palm down, across the front of the partner's chest and senses the amount of movement in the area of Thoracic Expansion, feeling for the elevation and protrusion of the upper chest. Then the explorer holds the sides of the partner's rib cage and senses the amount of movement in the area of Thoracic Expansion, feeling for the sideways elevation and protrusion of the chest. Then the explorer places a hand, palm down, on the partner's belly and senses the amount of movement in the area of Abdominal Expansion, feeling for the protruding and receding of the abdominal paunch.

The explorer then encourages the partner to increase movement in areas where there is little expansion and decrease movement where there is a lot of expansion, whilst the partner observes how this influences feelings and sensations.

whose voice is habitually stuck in Flute Timbre. Thoracic Expansion, meanwhile, tends to coincide with Clarinet Timbre and Configuration; and Saxophone Timbre and Configuration is nearly always coincident with Abdominal Expansion. In fact, it is very difficult to expand the voice tube and create the rich booming resonance of the Saxophone Timbre without drawing upon the movement of the abdominal region.

Component two – pressure

The second ingredient which makes up the Breathing Pattern is the degree of Pressure with which air is inspired and expired. Some people draw air in with incredible suction, as though they are drowning for lack of oxygen. People who breathe in this way are often insecure and find it difficult to trust the environment. They inspire with great inward Pressure like a starving prisoner eating a meal before it is taken away. This way of inspiring makes it difficult for them to relax and enjoy the food of life. However, people who breathe in this way are also usually those blessed with quick and responsive impulses who respond well to the needs of the moment.

Other people inspire with a mild suction as though there is no threat of extinction. People who breathe in this way are often lethargic and sedentary and find it hard to mobilize the energy necessary to seize the moment. However, people who inspire with little effort also tend to be those who are able to relax and find security amongst the hubbub.

Some people expire forcefully, pushing breath out under great Pressure, as though desperate to be rid of the air within. We all do this when we are irritable or angry and people who breathe habitually in this way are often carrying a lot of buried rage. People who breathe in this way tend to be those who know how to express strength and who have no trouble expiring the winds of anger. For those who do have trouble in stirring the hurricane of their fury, breathing with great Pressure can act as a catalyst for the release of unchartered anger. Conversely, for those whose anger is perched permanently on the edge of their tongue and who wish to find a more gentle approach to life's stimuli, decreasing the Pressure of the breath can have a calming and assuaging effect.

Other people expire in a prolonged and gentle way, as though indulging the collapse of their lungs. We all do this when we are disappointed or exasperated and many people who breathe habitually in this way are fundamentally disillusioned. However, people with

[
Voice Movement Therapy Exercise

Exploring Pressure

Stand or sit comfortably and notice the Pressure with which
you inspire and expire. Then gradually make changes,
increasing and decreasing this Pressure, noticing the way
different levels of Pressure influence how you feel. Then,
begin to vocalize and notice how different pressures of
breathing influence the quality of sound as you explore
various combinations of vocal ingredients.
]

unpressured expiration often also know how to enjoy the art of letting
go and are in no hurry to inspire more stimulation. For those who feel
understimulated and unenlivened, increasing the Pressure of the
breath can activate fresh desires and motivations. For those who are
overstimulated, on the other hand, decreasing the Pressure of the
breath can create a sense of clarity and serenity.

Generally, the higher the pressure of expiration the greater the
Loudness of the voice. To make changes to the habitual Loudness level
of the voice it is therefore necessary to revision the breathing pressure.

Frequency

The third ingredient which makes up the Breathing Pattern is
Frequency: that is how many times we breathe in and out over a given
unit of time.

Some people breathe quickly, taking many breaths in a minute as
though the clock of their soul is ticking at great speed. People who
breathe with speed are often quick to panic and can easily become
caught in a vicious circle where their anxiety increases respiratory
Frequency and in turn the increased speed of breathing amplifies
the anxiety.

A person's Frequency of breathing is deeply related to their sense of
time. The god of time in Greek mythology was Cronos, who ate his
own children; and those who breathe in quick time are often those
who feel eaten up by chronology, as though they have to rush to live
their lives before it is all over. Slowing down the Frequency of the
breath can therefore be very healing for such people, though it often
causes panic at first.

A high respiratory Frequency tends to keep the muscles of the body

Voice Movement Therapy Exercise

Exploring Frequency

Stand or sit comfortably and notice how many cycles of inspiration and expiration you make over a period of one minute. Then increase the respiratory Frequency for a further minute and notice how the accelerated speed of breathing influences your feelings and sensations. Return to your familiar respiratory Frequency for a little while to compare the difference. Now, decrease the respiratory Frequency of cycles for a further minute and notice how this decelerated speed of breathing influences your feelings and sensations. Finally, begin to vocalize and notice how different frequencies of breathing influence the quality of sound as you explore various combinations of vocal ingredients.

in a state of high tension, including the muscles which control the tension of the vocal cords. As a result, a greater respiratory Frequency can have the effect of tensing the vocal cords and causing a higher Pitch range than the range of those who breathe with less Frequency. There is then some relationship between the vibratory frequency of the vocal cords and the Frequency of the breath. For those who want to lower the Pitch range of their voice, it is therefore often necessary to decrease the respiratory Frequency, which has the effect of lessening muscle tension and imbuing the person with a sense of relaxation.

Volume

The fourth ingredient to the Breathing Pattern is Volume: that is literally how much air is inspired and expired.

The more air that is inhaled, the more the body has to expand to facilitate the expansion of the lungs; the volume of air people breathe is therefore connected to the degree they feel their own expansiveness. Those who find it difficult to take up space and claim their territory tend to breathe small volumes of air; while those with a developed sense of their presence tend to drink air in large quantities. For those who find it hard to claim a space and a territory which is expansive enough to hold the magnitude of their personality, increasing the Volume of breath is very healing. While those who feel that they flounder in the greatness of the world and who need to 'pull in the

Voice Movement Therapy Exercise

Exploring Volume

Stand or sit comfortably and breathe in and out through your mouth, imagining that the inspired air is a nourishing and tasteful liquid that you drink. Firstly, drink this liquid in small sips, taking in a very small quantity and notice how this affects your feelings and sensations. Then begin to vocalize and notice how breathing a minimal Volume influences the sound of your voice.

Now begin to drink in a larger cupful when you inhale and notice how the increased Volume of air affects your feelings and sensations. Then begin to vocalize and notice how breathing a greater Volume influences the sound of your voice.

Finally, gulp air in large quantities as though you are extremely thirsty and notice how this influences your feelings and sensations. Finally, vocalize and notice how the radically increased Volume of air changes the sound of your voice.

reins' and create a sense of privacy and personal intimacy, decreasing the Volume of breath can help to centre a person.

The amount of air which people breathe is also generally related to the amount of nourishment which they allow themselves. There is often an equation between the volume of air which a person breathes and the degree to which a person affords themselves the pleasures of life. For those who treat themselves frugally, increasing the Volume of breath helps to encourage a generosity of spirit towards the soul. While for those who tend to devour and consume at the expense of discernment, decreasing the Volume of breath can help to develop a modesty of appetite.

The greater the volume of air breathed in, the greater the volume of air breathed out; and the longer it takes to expire. Therefore, those who breathe with high Volume tend to be those who can vocalize long phrases; whilst those who breathe with less volume have to interrupt their vocalization more frequently with inspirations. Increasing the Volume of air can therefore give people the sense of being able to express more of themselves without interruption – and this can be extremely empowering.

Depth

The fifth ingredient to the Breathing Pattern is Depth: that is how deep or shallow the inspired breath is drawn into the lungs.

People who breathe with rapid Frequency and take in a small Volume of air tend to concentrate movement in the area of Thoracic Expansion but neglect the abdomen. This Breathing Pattern has the effect of exchanging the air at the top of the lungs but does not draw air down into the bottom. But the most efficient absorption of oxygen takes place at the bottom of the lungs because there are more blood vessels concentrated there. This shallow breathing therefore denies the body of oxygen and denies the psyche from feeling that nourishment is being drawn deep into its core. People who avoid breathing into the depth of their lungs are often those who have difficulty allowing themselves to be affected deeply by life's motion. They tend to exchange air with the world quite superficially, moving across the surface of many encounters but rarely absorbing the emotional atmosphere of other souls.

Other people tend to breathe with less Frequency, take in a greater Volume of air and consequently take the time to draw air down into the bottom of the lungs by expanding them downwards with the

Voice Movement Therapy Exercise

Exploring Depth

To begin, breathe in and out through your mouth focusing the movement in the area of Thoracic Expansion. Breathe with a moderate Pressure, quite a high Frequency and a moderate Volume. Notice how it feels as though the breath is only exchanged at the top of the lungs and focus on the feelings and sensations provoked by this shallow breathing. Begin to vocalize and notice the effect of breathing with little Depth on the voice. Now breathe in and out through your mouth focusing the movement in the area of Abdominal Expansion. Breathe with a moderate Pressure, quite a low Frequency and quite a lot of Volume. Notice how it feels as though the breath is now drawn down to the bottom of the lungs and focus on the feelings and sensations provoked by this deep breathing. Begin to vocalize and notice the effect of breathing with great Depth on the voice.

diaphragm. People with this Breathing Pattern tend to find it difficult to relate to the world lightly; they take everything in deeply and absorb emotions and atmospheres into their core. For those who find it hard to take life lightly and move quick-footed in the breeze, breathing with little Depth can help to create a sense of shallow enjoyment. For those whose healing journey is in search of greater depth of connection with the world and with themselves, however, breathing with great Depth is an essential requisite.

Many people have acquired the habit of shallow breathing in order to protect themselves against absorbing the negative charge of a hostile environment; often, they are those who grew up in a violent or unsafe atmosphere where they tried to breathe in as little of it as possible. Others with shallow breathing have experienced a trauma which 'took their breath away' and from which they have never recovered.

Those with deep breathing tend to vocalize in a lower Pitch range and in Saxophone or Clarinet Timbre; those with shallow breathing tend to vocalize in a higher Pitch range and in Flute Timbre. Changing the depth or shallowness of the Breathing Pattern can therefore influence the Pitch and Harmonic Timbre of the voice.

Tube configuration

The sixth ingredient to the Breathing Pattern is the shape and size of the tube: that is whether the tube is in Flute, Clarinet or Saxophone Configuration.

The Flute Configuration is so narrow that the air inside it is very pressurized; and those people who breathe habitually through a Flute Configuration tube are often those who feel that their emotions are dammed up under pressure and forever about to burst. In addition, it is impossible to breathe a large Volume of air through such a narrow tube which means those who breathe with a Flute Configuration tube have to breathe with great Frequency and exchange air at the top of the lungs with little Depth. At the other end of the spectrum, the Saxophone Configuration is so expanded that great Volumes of air pass in and out and people who breathe through such a configuration often feel that their emotions spill out without any sense of containment or reservation. Depending upon the predicament of the person, changing the configuration of the tube therefore not only alters the Harmonic Timbre of the sound but also affects the degree to which emotions feel reserved or expressed.

Breathing through Saxophone Configuration tends to encourage a slower Frequency with movement concentrated in the area of

Voice Movement Therapy Exercise

Exploring the Tube

Stand comfortably and breathe in and out through your mouth. Narrow the voice tube to Flute Configuration by blowing cool air as though to lower the temperature of hot food (*see* figure 8, page 61). Imagine that the voice tube is very narrow and that it extends from the lips down to the indent between the clavicles at the top of the breastbone. Notice how breathing through this configuration affects the other components of your Breathing Pattern and how this pattern affects your feelings and sensations.

Now open the mouth and dilate the throat and expand the dimensions of the voice tube to Clarinet Configuration by blowing hot air as though to steam up a pair of spectacles (*see* figure 9, page 62). Imagine that the tube extends from the lips down to the centre of the torso at the bottom of the breastbone.

Now expand the voice tube to its maximum dimensions, dilating mouth and throat as though yawning and imagine that the tube extends from the lips all the way down into the belly (*see* figure 10, page 63). Notice how breathing through this configuration affects the other components of your Breathing Pattern and how this pattern affects your feelings and sensations. Now, repeat the three configurations noticing how they influence the quality of sound as you explore different combinations of vocal ingredients.

Abdominal Expansion, exchanging air right to the bottom of the lungs. Breathing with Flute Configuration tends to encourage a faster Frequency with movement concentrated in the area of Thoracic Expansion, exchanging air at the top of the lungs. Therefore, changing the configuration of the tube influences the other components of the Breathing Pattern and can be used to assist the recomposition of the other components which make up the pattern to a healing end.

A breath of fresh air

As the breathing pattern changes through the healing process, it is very common for intense emotions to be released through sounds which the person may have never made or even heard before.

Breathing provides the core ingredient of the human voice. Many people are prevented from sounding good and feeling good because they are not making full use of their capacity to breathe. Some breathe with too little Depth, some with an overly rapid Frequency, some inhibit movement in the area of Thoracic Expansion, others do not allow movement in the area of Abdominal Expansion. While the various negative influences on breathing are manifold, the basic problem is simple: people do not breathe as well as they could. But by recognizing how we limit our breathing and by changing restricting respiratory patterns it is possible to enhance the way we feel and to positively influence the way we sound.

CHAPTER SEVEN

The Voice in Motion

*How the body sings and why moving in unfamiliar
ways can enhance the way we feel*

The soul in the soma

The body is our friend and our adversary. The body is our husband
and our wife; we are wedded to it until death parts us. Our body is the
temple of our spirit, the asylum of our pains and the home of our
pleasures. Our body is the keeper of our soul and when the psyche
speaks, her language is the language of the body. When we are afraid
it is because the tumbling juices in our belly tell us so. When we are
angry, it is because the rising audacity in our chest tells us so. When
we are mournful it is because the lump in our throat tells us so. When
our psyche is touched with emotion, our body is touched with sensation; and when our psyche is moved by feelings, our body is moved
into motion.

Stillness is possible for the body only in the moment of our death –
for even in the quietest hours the lungs exchange their tides with the
air, the heart beats out its refrain and the guts push all that we have
consumed further towards their ultimate expulsion. In these impera-
tive and mandatory movements lies the core of our feeling self, the
chemical underpinnings to our emotions, the somatic ballet which
accompanies the dance of our moods.

There is no expressive process which does not contain movement.
Motion is central to the way we experience ourselves as living souls.
We feel our thoughts, our sensations and our moods moving through
us and the word 'emotion' literally means to move something outwards. Physical movement of the body is therefore not just a means to
exercise the muscles, but also a way to activate the motion of our
imagination from the inner privacy of the self to expressive contact
with others.

Movement of the body always accompanies vocal expression, for
sound and action are part of the same process of communication. Yet
the pressures of every day life, the accumulation of muscular habits,
and the results of injury and misuse can leave us with a body which is

poorly able to express the vitality and intensity of the things we feel inside. Furthermore, the body is like a mask, it becomes fixed in certain attitudes until we move habitually and without the freedom for flexibility that we once had as children. Because the body houses the voice, fixed and rigid physicality often leads to limited vocal expression, which in turn creates the sense of an inflexible and fixed personality.

The self in space

The language of our innermost self is steeped in images of the body in space. We speak of sticking our neck out, putting our best foot forward, or of not having a leg to stand on. We keep our chin up and our nose clean. We bend over backwards to help someone and we get knocked sideways. We shoulder the blame, swallow our pride, foot the bill and kick the habit. We grasp the opportunity, lick our wounds, side-step the issue and tip-toe around the subject. We wriggle out of our commitments, shake loose from our responsibilities and leap through hoops to find a way out. We shelve ideas, jump into some things and run away from others. We get strung up, come close to the edge, feel boxed in, run around in circles and go up and down like a yo-yo. We feel like we are walking on broken glass, skating on thin ice and wading through mud. Things get on top of us, we feel snowed under and pushed into a corner. Life feels like a balancing act, we have too many balls in the air and the carpet gets taken from under our feet. We beat ourselves up over our mistakes and overstretch our resources. Some people waltz though life and others are constantly tripping over themselves. When we lose concentration we become 'spaced out'; mental anxiety creates a feeling of being 'on the edge'; in depression we feel 'down' and in elation we feel 'up'; and often our minds go round in circles. We conceive of the unconscious as being located in space beneath consciousness and the spiritual aspirations of the higher self as being vertically above the conscious psyche. In fact, the concept of self, psyche or soul remains very difficult to talk about without using images of space.

Images of the body in space also play an important role when it comes to describing vocal expression; and our body can feel impacted by what is said to us. We can feel poked, shaken or needled by someone's voice. We can feel tickled by an amusing remark and swiped by an insult. We feel that someone is twisting our arm, poking fun at our beliefs or knocking a hole in our argument. The voices of others who address us can cause us to feel stroked, held, blown away, put down or lifted up. Our voice rises up out of the inner space of our own body and literally hits the body of our audience with sound vibrations. The ear-drum is the most sensitive to these vibrations, but the entire surface of the body functions as an ear to some degree just as it did to a large extent in the womb. Voice is something which connects inner and outer environments and is a means by which we enter one another. Sound can make our bones shake.

Sound cannot be produced, cannot be amplified and cannot travel without space. The voice is produced within the space of the larynx; it is amplified by all the tiny spaces in the skull, face and torso as it travels through the tubular space of the throat and mouth; and then it travels through the open space around us before entering into the space of a listener's auditory canal. Space is an essential component of sound as well as being integral to the way we understand our soul. Everybody has an ongoing relationship with their own sense of space. Everyone is aware of having more or less room for the expression of their own personality. Each person is encircled by their own private Spherical Space. We are enveloped by a sphere of influence, a sphere of sensation, a sphere of selfhood. When someone approaches us, we feel

Voice Movement Therapy Exercise

Making Spherical Space

Go to a part of the room where you feel comfortable. Stand still with arms hanging loosely by your sides and imagine that you are in the centre of a sphere. Then venture forwards and backwards, side to side, and up and down, making hands-on contact with the imagined internal curved surfaces of the surrounding Spherical Space (*see* figure 15).

As you plot out the boundaries of your sphere, imagine that you are touring the contours of your psychic skin. Imagine the skin of your sphere to be made of a particular material and to be specifically coloured and consider that this may be a metaphor for the nature of your own psychic sensitivity, its permeability, its strength and fragility, its colourful vitality and its faded hue. Allow yourself to experience the sensation that you are safely contained by a private sphere of space.

As you move through your sphere, notice how specific places within it arouse particular feelings. You may experience a radical difference in mood when you are close

Voice Movement Therapy Exercise

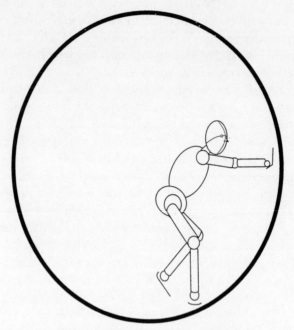

Figure 15 **Making Spherical Space**

to the back of your sphere compared to those feelings which are provoked by being close to the front. The back of the sphere may provoke sensations of withdrawal, depression, introversion and fear; or it may offer security, protection and a sense of confident stability. The front of the sphere may cause you to feel unnerved, exposed and dangerously unprotected; or you may experience this place as liberating and a place from which you could be seen and heard.

Now imagine that your torso is itself a sphere. Breathe in and out through your mouth and imagine that your lips form an opening to a tube that passes down into your torso which is filled with air during inspiration and emptied during expiration. Continue moving through your personal sphere and allow the spectrum of feelings provoked by specific locations to influence your breathing.

Now, as you journey through your sphere, begin to vocalize on the expired breath, exploring the complete palette of vocal ingredients.

them enter our sphere as we experience the arrival of another presence in our space. And when we approach another person, we make contact with them long before we touch them or hear them as we sense the elliptical atmosphere which orbits them like a galaxy. Spherical Space creates the atmosphere and architecture of our own world.

Spherical space

Each of us has learned to respond to the space around us; and this learning is primarily influenced by the nature of the environment in which we spent our early years. An infant learning to crawl and walk in an environment of damp and cold has a different journey to a child moving through a dry and warm landscape. The emotional fabric of the environment is influential also. A child surrounded by a cacophony of emotional conflict has his or her movements shaped by fear and anxiety. Meanwhile, a child moving through a landscape of love and tolerance is more likely to develop a physical expression free from the symptoms of anxiety. The acoustic fabric of the infant's environment also influences physical muscularity. The surrounding sound forms an audio-phonic enclosure. An acoustic envelope which is harsh and discordant penetrates the ears and psyche of the infant in a different way to sounds that are consistent, smooth and enfolding. And the neurological response to sound influences muscle use. Some sounds cause tension and contraction and others instil relaxation. How we move is influenced by what we heard.

As we grow to adulthood, a vestige of this early environment of infancy is carried with us, surrounding us wherever we go. The anxieties, fears, worries, insecurities and the sense of safety, security and consistency which constituted the play-room stay with us. Our adult world is, in many respects, still experienced as though we were crawling about in the world of our first home. The first impressions are the hardest to shake off; and the way we move through the world is coloured and impacted by the impressions we formed when we moved through our first environment. The memories of these early experiences are an impressionistic complex of sound, motion and feeling; and the acoustic memories are highly potent, for hearing is the first sense to be stimulated in our development. The degree to which we feel safe, held and supported and the degree to which we feel negatively impeded, threatened and insecure in the womb and afterwards in the Spherical Space of the sonorous envelope created between mother and infant, influences the way we will experience every environment through which we move thereafter. As adults, we still, to a certain extent, experience the environment around us as being coloured by the same factors which constituted our early spaces. Consequently, we move as though through our own Spherical Space which influences our physical and emotional expressions.

Although we move through the actual physical space of our environment as it is at any moment, we are also enclosed by the memory of early space. This space is like a little world which surrounds our body; it is a sphere of influence or a kinesphere. As we bend, curl and turn, so the Spherical Space of our personal envelope bends, curls and turns with us. We all move through the world within a private sphere which contains us until we die. We each carry with us a sphere which surrounds us 360 degrees and which is populated by fears, anxieties, constrictions and inhibitions, threats and obstacles. We can experience the Spherical Space of another person when we approach them and begin to sense the quality of presence which they radiate. Each person emits a certain atmosphere, a quintessential self that is emotionally charged and which influences our perception of their personality. The psychological atmosphere which weaves the fabric of our surrounding Spherical Space is therefore also 'trans-sensate' – it is beyond the senses.

The boundaries of our personal sphere form a psychic skin which create boundaries between our self and others and is primary in shaping the expression of our personality. Some people feel so permeable that their sensitivity can be excruciatingly painful; as though they have no skin. Others feel so thick-skinned that they find it difficult to sense the emotional qualities of others, or indeed of themselves. Many people have had their original boundaries disrespected and invaded through abuse. Others have never really been offered the sacred right to experience a personal sphere of dignity around their self in the first place.

Our sense of Spherical Space influences the way we move through life. Some people move as though they are compressed into a tiny sphere without room to move or breathe. Others inhabit a sphere so large that they seem to spill out in all directions without a feeling of containment. There are times when we are hemmed in, compressed, stifled and other times when we experience the spaciousness of our personality and self. There are also times when we seem to limit the size of our sphere deliberately, as though pulling in the boundaries and the limits of our self for protection and control. Some people move through life as though timidly crouching at the back of the sphere, avoiding direct confrontation with the world. Other people move as though always at the front of the sphere never knowing when to back off. Some people move as though precariously balancing at the edge of their sphere, barely holding themselves together. Others are so grounded in the centre of their sphere that they never touch the fringes of vulnerability. Of course, our sense of space changes as time passes. One day we may occupy a large sphere within which we stand firm and centred. Other days we may shrink the size of our sphere and occupy the backwaters.

Our sense of space also influences our voice; for giving voice is our way of making the space to be heard. For many people, they feel simply that this space does not exist. For some, their space is too small to create any echo or reverberation and their voice seems to be pushed inside of them and corked. For others, their Spherical Space is too big

Voice Movement Therapy Exercise

Voice Dancing the Sphere

Create a Spherical Space, plotting out the boundaries with your hands. Return to the centre of the sphere and breathe in and out through your mouth imagining that the inside of your torso is an inflatable sphere. Then begin to vocalize freely, experimenting with different combinations of vocal ingredients.

Now, as you vocalize, use the music of your voice as an accompaniment to an improvised dance. Firstly, begin dancing as though your sphere is a temple: move with graceful and solemn worship, kneeling, sitting, standing, genuflecting and allowing the body to give expression to a religious sphere. Now dance as though the sphere is a beach: run barefoot upon the sand, feel the sea breeze in your hair and roll upon the sand. Now imagine that your sphere is a forest: forage in the undergrowth and twist around the trees. Now imagine that your sphere is a busy street: dart in and out of other people and walk quickly and intently towards your destination.

Now begin to allow your sphere to transform into different environments of your choice, allowing the idea of the landscape to alter the way you move. As you pursue this, let your voice be affected by the changing modes of physical movement, giving voice to the environment of your sphere.

95

and they feel that their voice is lost in the abyss, like singing into a desert.

The inside of the body is also experienced as an inner space. The way people experience their voice is coloured by these inner spatial sensations and a familiar one is of a space that is blocked by an obstacle. Often, people talk about their voice being trapped behind a door, behind a wall or of it being locked inside a chest. Unlocking the voice means clearing space.

Over the past fifteen years I have witnessed many people take a healing journey through the use of Voice Movement Therapy techniques. And common to every journey has been the equation between sound and space. As people discover their voice, so they discover the space in which to sound themselves. For this reason, I very often ask people to create a private Spherical Space before pursuing an exercise and they move through this space as they journey through themselves. Creating a Spherical Space provides a delineated area within which you can give voice; and moving through this space in unfamiliar ways will enable you to give voice to yourself in unfamiliar sounds.

PART THREE

The Feeling Voice

CHAPTER EIGHT

Broken Hearts and Belly Laughs

*How crying and laughing are really songs in
disguise and how all feelings can and must be voiced*

Only people weep

Singers are experts at communicating the depths of joy and sorrow
through their voice. Yet everyone has the capacity to sing because
everyone has the capacity to laugh and to cry. When we laugh or cry,
we may not think that we are singing but we are. For laughing and
crying are among the few occasions when we allow the spontaneous
and instinctive use of the voice to come into play.

Of all the animals in the forest and the jungle, only humans weep.
Neither canines, felines, equines, porcines or bovines can cry and
though all animals may feel pain, their eyes remain dry – for tears are
beyond them. The bear may growl and the cat may roar, the ape may
yelp and the elephant may snort – but only homo sapiens lament their
sorrows with salt waters. Crying is a blessing which makes us human.
Crying is a gift which has been given to each of us so that others may
never be silent to the music of our moods. Crying is like bleeding: it lets
the inner liquid of our passions seep through. Crying is the torrent of
the soul and reminds us that the river of our heart runs deep.

Babies cry for what may seem like hours without end. But as time
evolves us towards maturity, crying becomes subject to legitimacies
and legislations which serve only to bind and chain us to our isolated
sufferings. Crying becomes something that we should only do in
private or at funerals. Crying becomes something more appropriate
for women than for men. Crying becomes a sign of weakness. At the
first sight of watery eyes people reach to donate their handkerchiefs
like amateur nurses – as though tears are something to be wiped up,
wiped away and damned.

There is a culture in Papua New Guinea where the word for crying
is also the word for singing, where there is no delineation between
weeping and singing, where all songs are rooted in different kinds of
crying and where you cannot sing if you do not cry and you cannot cry
without your weeping being heard as song. In all cultures, the singer is
a psychological symbol and represents the capacity to celebrate our

crying. One of the tasks that the singer takes upon his or herself is to make music from weeping. When we listen to a singer working from the soul, what we hear is crying made into an art form. With every cadence and crescendo, and every trill and vibrato, with every glide and call, we hear someone crying in public, turning droplets of tears into a trickle of notes.

Of mice and men

Unfortunately there are those whose tears have dried up in the heat of life's scorching blaze and who, knowingly or not, suffer the impoverishment which comes from the lack of weeping. Yet everyone can reclaim their ability to cry and the impulse may be provoked by something seemingly trivial. For when we are children, our tears are not provoked by tragedies of enormity but by the little things which are so important to us when we are little ourselves.

A man I once worked with called John provides a touching example of the magnitude of such small remembered things. John was a clear, confident and eloquent speaker and felt at ease introducing himself to the Voice Movement Therapy group. He could raise his voice in Loudness with no trouble; he could assert both his strength and his opinions and could readily mobilize himself to anger, which he expressed through the booming resonant tones of his voice. However, John did not cry. In fact, John confessed that he never felt sadness, sorrow or any sensation that might move him to tears; and this had started to bother him. His healing journey was to reclaim his weeping.

On the first day of the workshop John had written a Memory Song about a pet rabbit which he had when he was a child. On the second day, I worked with John individually and asked him to sing a single note gently into the palm of his hand and to imagine that he had a wounded rabbit in his palm. His voice was in Modal Register with quite a lot of Violin, in Clarinet Timbre but with no Free Air. As John sang, I asked him to mime stroking the rabbit with his other hand. To see this six-foot-tall man with shoulders broad enough to bare a nation uttering such sweet and gentle tones was a truly stirring sight.

As John sang I noticed tiny rhythmical spasms in his abdomen and so I placed my hand gently on his belly. As I did this he let out a long sigh as though something had changed gear. His voice now undulated with a gentle Pitch Fluctuation and became full of Free Air, as though a gate had opened, allowing his breath to come pouring through. I asked John to raise the Pitch of the note and to decrease the Loudness, as though he did not want to frighten the tiny creature in his hand. I suggested that he was the Rabbit Healer, a lone outcast that lived in the forest without human contact but who could communicate with the animals. He looked at me with inquisitive resonance as though in an uncanny way I had touched on something close to his soul. John's voice now began to break between Modal and Falsetto Register; his shoulders hunched and he began walking around the studio, as though alone in the forest. John began singing the words to his Memory Song in this new voice that was quiet, high in Pitch with a gentle Fluctuation, full of Free Air and which sobbed back and forth between the two Registers.

> Gentle one you have been hurt and no one really knows
> At the bottom of the garden we talk in rabbit speak and our
> friendship grows
> My world is hidden between these trees
> I don't like boys or girls
> But to be alone with my tiny friends
> Is all I really need

John said that he felt embarrassed by his song and the triviality of the memory; yet he was clearly choked and I supported him in continuing to sing. Then, in the middle of the song as his voice broke out of Modal into Falsetto, John began to cry. The more he cried, the more emotive and provocative his voice became and a number of people in the witnessing group were now also moved to tears.

John later said that while singing into the palm of his hand he had remembered how, as an only child who was awkward and often ridiculed at school, he had found solace in animals. In particular, he remembered playing for hours at the bottom of the garden where he would talk to his rabbits in a pretend make-believe language. Somehow this simple memory, provoked by finding the space to place his body and voice back in that garden, had unlocked tender emotions which he had not allowed himself to express since a child: feelings of loneliness, sorrow, and despair.

Orpheus in the underworld

John's tears were an expression of his sense of loss. For he had lost the tender and sorrowful parts of himself and had covered his crying with a brave smile and a bombastic persona. The little boy who loved rabbits and felt the human pangs of loneliness was buried beneath layers of self-sufficiency. Our crying is intimately connected to our sense of loss. The first cries of the baby express a grieving for the lost womb and we go on crying our losses until the day we die.

The relationship between singing and grieving is encapsulated powerfully in the story of the Greek hero Orpheus, who is the classical symbol of song as well as representing the inevitability of human loss. Orpheus was born to the god Apollo and his lover Calliope, and from the moment he was born he sang out with a golden voice that amazed everyone. When it was time for Orpheus to leave home, his father gave him a lyre so that Orpheus could accompany his beautiful singing.

One afternoon, whilst Orpheus was passing through a forest, he noticed a beautiful woman dancing and fell in love with her at first sight. This woman's name was Eurydice. But at the height of their delicious love affair on a hot sunny day, Orpheus fell asleep in a lemon grove while Eurydice was picking berries. It was here that according to some she was raped and according to others she was poisoned by a serpent. Whichever is true, she was taken to the Underworld, the land of the dead ruled by a relentless figure called Hades.

When Orpheus discovered the fate of his beloved he despaired, because he knew that no one living could enter the Underworld and once there, no one could return. Yet, he thought of his voice and its powers. He reflected upon how he had used his voice to calm aggressors, to assuage storms, to seduce lovers and to talk to the beasts. Perhaps, thought Orpheus, his voice would be powerful enough to guide him into the Underworld and rescue his dear Eurydice.

Fearless and determined, Orpheus followed his lover's footsteps down through the face of the earth and into the Underworld. He met Charon the Ferryman whom he had to persuade to transport him across the river Styx; he met Cerberus the three-headed hound of Hades; and he encountered hellish characters and terrifying monsters. But each time he met a new obstacle he drew upon his voice and sang with such power and such heart that his aggressors cleared the path and pointed him to his destination.

When Orpheus reached the centre of the Underworld he met face to face with Hades and pleaded with him to let Eurydice return to the light of the living world with him. Hades was so struck by the urgency of Orpheus' love and so moved by the spirit of Orpheus' voice that he agreed to let him take Eurydice with him – on one condition. Orpheus was not to turn back to look at Eurydice until they were both back upon the earth.

Wasting no time, Orpheus proceeded back the way he had come, with Eurydice following closely behind him. They travelled again through gorge and crag, across the river Styx and back up towards the earth's floor. But, with only a short distance left to travel, Orpheus could no longer resist and he turned to gaze upon his lover. In this moment Eurydice was snatched by the winds of the Underworld and Orpheus lost her for ever. So grief stricken was Orpheus that he cried and cried and cried and his cries led to songs which echoed throughout the lands for an eternity.

Songs of loss and longing

On the surface of the story, Eurydice is Orpheus' lover. But psychologically she is more than this, for she represents a part of his soul that is lost and must be reclaimed. It is natural to wonder why Orpheus turned to look at Eurydice; for surely he would have heard her footsteps behind him. We can only imagine that Orpheus did not trust his ears as much as his eyes. Perhaps that was the downfall. For we cannot look at our soul. We cannot turn and gaze upon it. The soul cannot be seen, it is not visible and cannot be located, dissected, placed under the microscope and observed. The soul will not subject itself to an autopsy, which means to see automatically with the eye. The soul evades the eye; and the more we attempt to look at the soul the more it escapes our understanding and our grasp. Though light enlightens it also burns; and the delicacy of the soul's fabric must be protected from the scorching rays of the inquisitive lamp. This was the lesson that Orpheus learned. Eurydice was in his trail; yet he could not trust the sound of her footsteps. Neither did he trust himself to use his most precious gift – his voice – to call her. He had to turn to look, to gaze, to see. And, caught by the terrifying light of his gaze, the poor soul was taken for ever.

If we want to solicit the company of the soul then we must refrain from placing it under the light of our gaze. We must stave off our optical fascinations and learn to listen to the soul instead. For though the soul is invisible it is not inaudible. We can perceive the soul with our ears. In fact the word 'audience' does not mean those who see but those who hear.

Because the soul is invisible and makes itself known through sound, we have to trust our own ears if we are to hear the language of the soul. And the language of the soul to which our ears must be open is the language of the human voice. This instrument with which we are all blessed is, as Orpheus discovered, capable of calming and placating monsters. And of course the monsters by which we are most threatened are the monsters in our own selves: the monsters we call depression and anxiety, the monsters we call guilt and shame, the monsters we call shyness and loneliness, the monsters that inhibit us and enrage us; and the monsters that we call loss and grief which were the most daunting

Voice Movement Therapy Exercise

Crying Song, Laughing Song

Create a Spherical Space and map out the four points of a compass, limbering your body and exploring your Breathing Pattern.

Consider what happens to your breath, body and voice when you cry. Then, see if you can raise your weeping by emulating this pattern of breathing, movement and sound. Inhale as though you were sobbing, enact the gestures that you use when you are awash with tears and vocalize as you do when you cry. Let the voice tremor with a Pitch Fluctuation and allow it to break between Modal and Falsetto Registers. Now, expand the voice tube to Saxophone and let the voice sob with lots of Free Air.

Now begin to focus on a particular subject or a particular set of feelings and allow lyrics to flow. Then, begin to develop your vocalization into a melody and allow a Crying Song to emerge.

Write out the words to your Crying Song and sing them with a combination of vocal ingredients which enable you to musicalize your crying.

Now consider what happens to your breath, body and voice when you laugh. Then, see if you can raise your laughter by emulating this pattern of breathing, movement and sound. Inhale as though you were laughing, enact the gestures that you use when you are adrift in amusement and vocalize as you do when you laugh. Let the voice tremor with a Pitch Fluctuation and allow it to break between Modal and Falsetto Registers. Now, expand the voice tube to Saxophone and let the voice guffaw.

Now begin to focus on a particular subject or a particular set of feelings and allow lyrics to flow. Then, begin to develop your vocalization into a melody and allow a Laughing Song to emerge.

Write out the words to your Laughing Song and sing them with a combination of vocal ingredients which enable you to musicalize your laughter.

of the monsters that Orpheus finally overcame through singing. All of the negative forces and influences to which we are prey are like the monsters that Orpheus met on his journey. And just as Orpheus calmed the monsters in his path with song, so too we can calm our own inner monsters through singing. Singing disperses fear and bandages our wounds. Singing lifts our spirits and settles our nerves. Singing discharges our emotions and animates the heart. Singing gives shape to a soul that cannot be seen.

Throughout my teachings, where I have had the opportunity to work with people from all walks of life, I have realized that everyone has, like Orpheus, lost a part of their soul; and for many many years now I have been accompanying people on their journey through the Underworld, helping them reclaim the lost parts of their soul through singing. Some people have lost their joy, others have lost a loved one, a relationship or a marriage; some have lost their trust and sense of safety due to a traumatic experience, others have lost their self-confidence and belief in themselves; some people have lost their sexuality and their vitality; others have lost their aggression and ability to assert themselves. And, some people have lost things which they never really had in the first place. For many of us have been denied the things we needed from the very start. But whether we have lost something that we once had or are grieving something we never possessed, we are all, like Orpheus, on a journey to reclaim what we need; and my job is to help people to do this through song.

Of laughter and forgetting

Laughter is a medicine for the heart. Laughter is an oil and a balm. Laughter steps in and lubricates when the muscle of the psyche becomes rigid; it challenges our seriousness and reminds us that sometimes the greatest gift we can give our own soul is to chuckle in its face. Laughter is airborne, like hydrogen it is lighter than oxygen and rises above the weighted heaviness of our own self-reflections. In some ancient cultures, people believed that laughter was carried on the wind and entered the soul through the ears. Once laughter had entered, all anyone could do was surrender to its infectious determination to bring havoc to order. Laughter is anarchic and creates a momentum which seems to escalate rapidly. In laughter, people will say what they may not have dared to say before. Laughter causes us to risk bringing the shadow into the light of day, exposing the dark wit of ridicule. Laughter is the animated face of wisdom. We laugh at what we know to be true. When we laugh it is because we get the joke, we see the light, we resonate with the truth. The symbol of the Buddha, whose belly was full of knowledge and whose face is always smiling, reminds us that where there is laughter there is wisdom. When we laugh from the belly, the iron scaffolding of our defences becomes demolished, the frown upon our brow and the analytical gaze of our eyes take respite as we take leave of our serious senses.

The sound of laughter is a bell that rings to tell the soul that it is play-time; and a life without laughter is a life without play. Just as we have never discovered a society of people who do not sing, neither has any-one ever discovered a culture without play. Play is a universal human act which fosters the spirit of the imagination. Play calls forth our inner capacity to invent, to pretend, to surpass the limitations forced upon us by the reality of circumstance. In play the poor may become rich, the meek may become strong, the powerful may be subordinated and an entire set of relations may be turned upside down and reinvented. In play, we are relieved of our usual mask and have an opportunity to discover the multiplicity of our self. In play we become actors with an endless cast of persons waiting in the wings of the psyche.

We speak of play in relation to playing an instrument; yet many musicians become so wedded to the rules of the game and the stric-tures of musicianship that they eventually awaken to the realization that they have been robbed of their original desire to play and be playful through their art. This can happen to singers too. I have worked with many singers whose voices have been made technically proficient by a thorough training regime but whose impulsive, emotive and intuitive self has been surreptitiously evacuated in the process. Such singers can no longer play with their instrument and can feel as though they are no longer connected to their voice.

Discovering the voice should be full of play. Though unchaining the vocal instrument from years of repression brings with it a torrent of emotions, many of them lamentable and sad, vocal liberation also releases the spirit of laughter and elation. Often when people begin to discover the range of their voice and the spectrum of sounds which they can make, a thousand characters, images, memories and emotions come flooding out of the mouth, as though an orchestra of a thousand instrumentalists has been awakened after a hundred years of sleep. Some of the sounds which people make in the process of discovering their voice are so outlandish and bizarre that they provoke ravenous and maniacal laughter. Other sounds carry with them such poignant and sorrowful recollections that they provoke a flooding cascade of cries. And both of these can bring tears to the eyes.

The tears of joy and the tears of sadness are very closely related; and often we can feel that our weeping and our laughter are so close together that we can barely tell them apart. I have witnessed many people who, in the moment of discovering a liberated voice, shed tears of sorrow and joy in a single moment; it is as though they have broken through into the realm of pure pathos where the complete palette of emotions weave together in a paradoxical tapestry. In this realm, feelings are experienced deeply and fully without the need to divide them into opposites.

The good woman

I worked with a woman called Brigitte whose healing journey involved the doleful and lamentable acknowledgement of her losses as well as the delightful and enchanted rediscovery of the spirit from which she had been separated. Hers was a journey that, like the journeys of many, touched the paradoxical core of tears that are shed in joy and sorrow simultaneously.

Brigitte was a good woman; she had been a good wife to her husband, a good mother to her two children and a good friend to all those in her circle. She had been hostess, envoy and confederate in attendance as she followed her husband around the globe in the service of his profession. At diplomatic parties she had been beguiling and graceful, exalting her husband's name and extolling the importance of his missions. She had stood at the side of rugby pitches and football grounds cheering her sons as they touched down and kicked off. She had listened to all of their stories, colluded in all of their antics and risen out of bed in the early hours of many mornings to fetch them back from alcoholic parties of adolescent debauchery, placing toast and orange juice at their table before they fell asleep between the cotton sheets that she ironed with obedient regularity.

Now Brigitte's husband had retired and her boys had left the nest. Brigitte was lost, a little dazed and without the sense of purpose or function which had guided her for so long. Though nobody had died she was in bereavement.

Brigitte began to make a sound. Her chest raised as she inhaled, her eyes sparkled and she intoned a long note that was fragile, light and quivered with a shaky tentativeness. Her voice was full of Free Air and Pitch Fluctuation and as she vocalized I placed my hand upon her chest and exerted a little pressure. This caused Brigitte's voice to increase substantially in Loudness and as she sang I felt the imploring for reassurance in her eyes. 'It's OK,' I said, 'just let it flow from your heart.' It was then that Brigitte emitted a tirade of sobbing. She blub-bered and howled as her chest rose and fell like an elevator passing up and down through the Tower of Babylon. The Frequency and the Volume of her Breathing Pattern increased and she began exaggerat-ing the area of Abdominal Expansion. Her face become showered with the waters of her tears. A backlog of feeling that had been stored up behind her eyes poured down like rain.

As she cried I noticed that her voice traced a five-note melody which she repeated each time she expired. Holding her close to me with my arm around her shoulders and my other hand still placed firmly upon her chest I sang the melody with her, encouraging her to expand upon it. Within a few minutes she was singing and crying at the same time, her cheeks red, her eyes wet, her voice resounding like a bassoon. Her voice passed fluidly from low notes to high. In Falsetto Register her voice gleamed and shone like a golden fleece. In Modal Register her voice folded and churned like hot maple syrup. Then she stopped and began to laugh. I laughed with her, 'I don't know why I am crying,' Brigitte whispered as she chuckled, 'I am not really sad about anything.' I looked into her eyes and smiled and asked her if she could think of a song that we could work with. She said that she recalled a song which she had heard many times on the radio. She thought the song was called 'Why Do You Never See Me Crying', but she was not sure. However, she had heard it so many times, she could remember the words of the first half.

Brigitte stood tall, her eyes still damp and her cheeks still flushed as she sang this song, as she remembered it, with poise and remorse, with zeal and yearning.

> Why is it that you never seem to see
> The tears that roll and trickle down my cheeks
> I could cry an ocean and turn my heart to dew
> And all of my sweet sorrows would still escape you.
> I can feel a river of regret run through my soul
> Yet still I do believe that I can make it through,
> If only I could learn to cry and smile with the joy
> Of knowing that though my heart aches
> I'm alive because I feel
> It's my philosophy that this crying that is me
> Is better than the cold dry winds of an empty heart.
> But still I am sad that you never seem to see
> The tears that roll and trickle down my cheeks.

The group watched and listened and in the moments after the song came to its end there was a viscous silence which preceded the appreciative applause.

Later that day, Brigitte spoke of how she felt in some way bereaved. She had laid down so much of herself serving her husband and sons and in the process had lost her voice in a family of male voices. Now her husband and sons no longer pulled upon her service, she also felt bereaved without her role as mother and wife. Her identity had melted and there seemed nothing to take its place. Her crying had been both an expression of her grief and at the same time a reclaiming of her own voice of feminine pathos. It was herself that she was crying over. She had always wanted to hear herself sing but never thought she could, never thought she would. For the remainder of the three-week Voice Movement Therapy course she carried around her an air of serenity and sang many songs as well as laughing and crying daily.

Don't dam the flood

Often, when we weep, we stop ourselves from fully releasing the voice of our crying and consequently we never really emancipate the part of ourselves which is drowning in our unshed tears. The throat cracks, the breath breaks and the waters flow but then we inhale and swallow and retract the emerging crescendo. It is as though crying is accompanied by guilt or fear. Guilt that we should snap out of it, snap to it and snap back into the mediocrity of life's veneer. Fear that if we allow ourselves to enter without apology into the music of our crying we will explode or garrotte our heart or overwhelm those around us with an unceasing flood. Often the tendency of others is to step in and impede the current of our cries with handkerchiefs, kind words and ameliorating remarks. Other people's crying can frighten us, make us uneasy and provoke our own pained displeasure.

If we do not allow ourselves to cry unabated, then the pressure of the passionate waters builds up inside our chest and pushes against the walls of our torso from the inside. We feel as though we are always about to burst, always damned up and stressed, and we long for an opportunity to depressurize, to bleed away the steam arising from the simmering stew of unsounded emotions.

Often, when I place my hands upon someone's chest, as I did with Brigitte, I can feel the force of the emotional waters pushing against my palms. When I listen to the voice I can hear both the desire to release the rhapsody and cacophony of these feelings and the terror of what might happen if the chest were to collapse and the torrent to flow from the throat in sound. When the waters break it is my job to be there to bail away the excess, to hold the person in sway upon the tide and to stand firm – as mast and compass, navigator and lighthouse. It is a duet not a solo; and anyone seeking to assist another person in the release of such primary emotions in sound must be well equipped and experienced in charting the unpredictable nature of the rocky seas.

CHAPTER NINE

Unlocking the Lion in our Hearts

*Why animals don't need to talk and how to voice our
primal instincts*

The beast that spoke

We have evolved out of our primitive past over thousands of years
to become the most highly sophisticated, thoughtful and multi-
dimensional beings on earth. We have enhanced the powers of the
mind to such a degree that it is capable of great ingenuity, perception
and calculation. We can compute the distance of the stars from earth,
predict the behaviour of sub-atomic particles and transplant major
organs from one human body to another. The possession of this
highly evolved mind sets us apart from other animals; and the most
poignant symbol of the special place which we hold amongst the
beasts is language. To be without articulate speech is to be without a
prided human faculty.

On 26 May 1828, a strange figure who seemed to be part animal
and part man staggered into Unschlitt Square in Nuremberg. He was
weeping and his face expressed intense pain. He seemed to hear without
understanding, to see without perceiving and his language consisted
of moans, groans and sobs. His body was that of a young man and his
behaviour that of a small child. The only difference of opinion among
those who gathered around this poor soul was whether he should be
regarded as a madman, an idiot or a kind of savage. This strange
character was given the name Kaspar Hauser and was educated by a
Professor Daumer who taught him to speak. Nobody knows the truth
of Kaspar's history; but legend has it that he was an illegitimate child
who was locked away in a dark stable for the first sixteen years of his
life to save his wealthy mother's family from embarrassment.

Kaspar Hauser is one of many children who have been discovered
roaming the wilds and who have been adopted by the benefactors of
civilized society; and they have all had one thing in common. All of
these savage children who have been rescued or removed from their
wild surroundings were unable to speak; and their desperate grunts
and groans, sobs and wails frightened some and intrigued others. But

everybody who met these wild children shared the opinion that if these creatures were to be civilized they must be taught to speak. Those without language are considered to be dumb – which means both mute and stupid. When an array of kind and charitable benefactors sought to bestow upon Kaspar and others like him the ability to speak, they believed that through the powers of language these children could become civilized. Throughout human history, we have been proud to set ourselves apart from other beasts, for we are the only animal that speaks. Language is the symbol of our sophistication.

The lives of those such as Kasper Hauser remind us of an earlier time in human development when we may not have been as mentally evolved as we are now. Despite the enormous cerebral ingenuity that we have developed, we remain animals, closer to the beasts than our minds would care to admit. Our psyches are driven by a team of wild horses and though they are reined to our thoughts they long to be free. Like all animals we host instincts that, if the occasion calls, will disobey the taming influence of reason and tear our soul through the air like a mythical chariot. And the language of this instinct is not words but voice.

When a mother sees her child stray to the middle of a busy road she yells with a ferocity normally unknown to girl or woman, for the instinct to protect is preserved at the animal level. When a soldier loses a comrade to a mortar shell in the trenches, he howls with an electrifying sound normally unknown to boy or man, for the instinct of companionship is preserved at the animal level. When pushed to the limits of exasperated intimidation, we may all screech and bellow, bark and blare at the top of our voices, unleashing our seldom-used acoustic weaponry like a lion, for the instinct of retaliation is preserved at the animal level.

The human animal stands at a crossroads, a psychic intersection with one road leading to the well of instinct and the other to the nerve centre of thought. Here we stand contemplating our choices without a map and without a compass. Neither road can serve our search for enlightenment. The road to instinct reminds us too much of our primitive past and all that is uncontrollable and savage for it to be an inviting option. Yet, the road to thought threatens us with the colourless tedium of abstraction devoid of danger and spontaneity. Thus we stand bemused like Oedipus before the Sphinx, wondering how we can solve the riddle and have both our thoughts and our instincts, our head and our guts.

For many of us, the relationship between our cognitive thoughts and our instinctual drives is adversarial and contentious, both of them battling for possession of our senses. This battle between thought and instinct is played out between word and voice and our throat can often feel like the firing range of this war. Our instincts rise up from the belly in the form of urgent sounds as our thoughts descend from the head in the form of articulate words. Both must pass through the throat in order to emerge. But it is rare that thought and instinct share the same intent or express the same desire; and often the thoughts which descend from the head fight against the instincts which rise from the belly. Consequently, the war in the throat leaves us confounded and bewildered as we gag and falter in our attempt to play arbitrator and umpire in the battle between the voice of our animal intuition and the language of our human comprehension.

Often what emerges from this battle is a compromise of such diluted consistency that neither our instincts nor our thoughts adequately resound and we go through life feeling unseen, unheard and unvoiced. We don't quite find the right words and we don't quite manage to underscore them with the right voice. We feel rage but voice only a mild irritation; we feel an overwhelming loneliness but voice only a moderate desire for company; we feel helpless but voice only a genial difficulty in managing the day ahead; we feel overwhelmed with excitement but voice only a gentle pleasure. For others among us, the voice is even further from the truth of our experience. In rage we voice tolerance; in loneliness we voice independence; in helplessness we voice accomplished competence; in excitement we voice a bland disengagement.

Often the lack of an instinctive voice stems from an ingrained fear of the animal passion, which originates in our early life. We may fear that if we voice our ecstasy and rapture, the source of our pleasure may be taken away; so we keep our excited voice of elation under wraps and replace it with an innocuous and dull appreciation. We may fear that if we voice our rage we may annihilate those who have provoked our fury; so we keep our rage clamped and clenched and replace it with a benign annoyance.

Our instincts are the shadow of our intelligence; and because we have intensified the light of our mental knowledge with such manifold compulsion, we have inevitably increased the density of our instincts to the same degree so that they now loom behind us wherever we turn. To fight them is like battling our shadow. To extinguish them we would have to demolish ourselves. To ignore them would be idiocy. To invite them to take partners with our thoughts, to assume equal place at the table is the only option capable of guiding us fruitfully forward to the blessings which are intended for us. Every intellectual dinner is a Bacchanalian feast in disguise; and every animal devouring is a discriminating Apollonian banquet in the making.

The psychic menagerie

Animal metaphors provide a vivid representation of qualities integral to our human nature: sly as a fox, cunning as a shrew, stubborn as a mule, slow as a snail, dog tired, strong as an ox, beavering away, slippery fish, dirty rat, filthy pup, lion-hearted, lone wolf, dark horse, stupid ass, fly like an eagle, feeling sluggish, frightened as a rabbit. We look to animals to provide an image of our instinctual passions; and working with the full range of the human voice is a way of permitting the downtrodden animality of our instincts into the light of day.

There is no doubt, we have lost the primal power of the human voice, and language is largely to blame. Moreover, there is considerable fear in many people about unleashing vocal power; few things cause such immediate reticence, embarrassment and constriction than the attempt to yell, shout and sing out in rage and fury, in grief and despair. Most primitive utterances of animality, such as yawning and belching, literally lead us to putting our hands over our mouths. Perhaps this is because the preverbal and spontaneous utterances of the unformed and untamed voice remind us of the instinctive, primal and untamed aspects of ourselves which, deep down, still growl like the bear, roar like the lion and screech like the hawk. If so, then relocating and reanimating the close, sympathetic relationship we once had with the animals and their spirit or essence could provide us with the means to overcome those ever-so civilized structures of decorum, etiquette and social grace that keep our voices, and therefore our souls, enslaved.

To reclaim the breadth of our instincts we do well to borrow from the naïve wisdom of preverbal peoples and relocate the ancient part of our being that longs to roar, snarl, holler, squawk, screech, moan, whimper, wail, bellow, shriek, call, hoot, hiss, bleat, snort, howl, cry and bay at the moon; in short to be the animals we are.

There are four main animal species which are central to our psychic fantasy life and which have filled the dreams of men and women for thousands of years: the ape, the lion, the wolf and the bird. Each of these animals represents a different set of human instincts and propensities; and stories of people turning into apes, lions, wolves and birds abound. Deep down we have an empathy for animals and these four seem to hold a special resonance for us. In Voice Movement Therapy, part of the healing process involves giving physical shape and vocal sound to these animal essences. Through this process of somatically and sonically identifying with our animal confederates, we can come to embody our instincts and feel their visceral power in our bones.

Voice Movement Therapy Exercise

The Animal Matrix

Create a Spherical Space and establish a centred and focused position in the centre of your sphere. Stand erect with legs straight, spine stretched vertically, arms hanging by the sides and eyes focused directly in front. Breathe in and out through a very narrow voice tube and maintain a facial expression of extreme concentration as you focus on your thoughts. Now, begin to vocalize in Flute Timbre. This position is called Homo Erectus and represents the sophisticated, cognitive and articulate human being (*see* figure 16a).

Now relax the knees and drop the pelvis towards the ground, allowing the arms to float outwards a little. Curve the spine into a concave arc with the centre of the chest imploded. Continue to breathe in and out through your mouth but allow the voice tube to expand to medium dimensions and begin to vocalize in Clarinet Timbre. As you make this change, allow your facial expressions to relax, your eyes to wander and shift the emphasis from a concentration of thought in the head to a sense of the feelings which reside in your heart. This position is called the Primate Position and provides an opportunity to identify with the great ape (*see* figure 16b).

Now drop forwards on to the hands and knees, let the abdomen relax and the belly hang down. Refocus your centre of experience away from the heart and towards the gut instincts in the belly. Allow your voice tube to expand to its maximum dimensions and begin to vocalize in Saxophone Timbre. This position is called the Feline-canine Position and provides an opportunity to identify with both the great cat and the wolf (*see* figure 16c).

Voice Movement Therapy Exercise

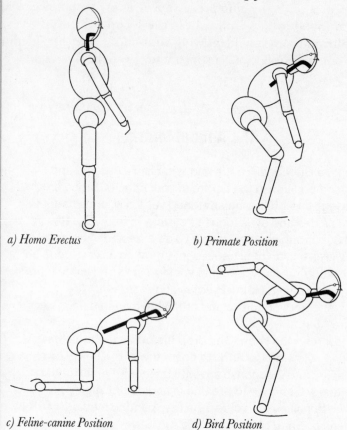

a) *Homo Erectus* b) *Primate Position*

c) *Feline-canine Position* d) *Bird Position*

Figure 16 **The Animal Matrix**

Now, come up towards a standing position but bend over from the waist and raise your arms behind you as though they are wings. Continue to vocalize in Saxophone Timbre but make the sound nasal, filling it with Violin. This position is called the Bird Position and provides an opportunity to identify with the great bird (*see* figure 16d).

Now you have identified the physicality and vocality of each animal position, travel round and round the cycle, moving from Homo Erectus to Primate, from Primate into Feline-canine, from Feline-canine into Bird, from Bird into Primate and from Primate back to Homo Erectus. Allow your voice to give expression to the range of instinctual passions which appear as you pass through the Animal Matrix.

Voice Movement Therapy Exercise

Now, as you continue to pass through the Animal Matrix, begin to personalize your exploration by following your empathy for other animals: reptiles, bovines, porcines, rodents as well as mythical creatures concocted from many beastly qualities. Allow your voice to travel to places which tap into the primality and animality of your being.

Then, as your journey reaches its end return to the Animal Matrix of Homo Erectus, Primate, Feline-canine and Bird and settle where you started in the erect concentrated position of the articulate thoughtful human being.

An end to 'Mother Goose'

Mary was a woman of petite proportion and slim dimension who spoke gently and quietly and who came to work with me because she had reached a point of extreme frustration at feeling 'worthless', 'unmotivated', 'unacknowledged' and somewhat 'taken advantage of'. She also complained of feeling very 'down' most of the time and 'all used up', as though she had no energy left. In addition, she suffered from an overwhelming shyness, a feeling of inferiority and what she described as a 'paralyzing lack of confidence'.

Mary had not had the opportunity for formal education beyond her late teens, despite a deep interest in and aptitude for the sciences. When she was fifteen her mother died and she was forced to look after her younger sister and brother. Shortly after her siblings had left home, her father had fallen ill with Parkinson's disease and she had nursed him until he died. During the period of nursing her father, she had met a man eight years her senior whom, after her father's death, she had married and with whom she had three children. Mary had enjoyed motherhood and she maintained a close relationship with her children. Shortly after her last child had left home, her husband became very ill with cancer and she nursed him for two years before he died. Since her husband's death, one year prior to our meeting, she felt 'completely at a loss'.

Mary felt that it was primarily through her voice, which she described as 'shaky', 'trembly' and 'thin', that her unassured personality was expressed; epitomizing this, she said that during her depressive periods she had remained 'almost dumb'. She also said that she had been told that she was 'too quiet', 'too slow' and that her voice was 'monotonous' and 'difficult to listen to' by a number of people close to her.

As Mary began toning single notes ascending and descending the Pitch scale, I noticed that her voice seemed to lack any frivolity or youth. Her voice was quite low in Pitch without any Free Air or Violin. It was in Flute Timbre and her complete range was in Modal Register. I asked Mary to try to imbue her voice with a quality of childlikeness. However, this was to no avail. We both agreed that her voice lacked a childlike spirit. It became apparent that Mary's childhood had been taken from her and she had been prematurely propelled into adulthood by the death of her mother, at which point she was forced to assume adult duties before her time. She had raised her younger sister and brother almost single-handedly and buried deep beneath Mary's brave face of 'having come to terms with this' there was an anger and a resentment which she felt she had put out of sight. So I asked Mary to sing the highest note of her comfortable Pitch range, imbuing it with an attitude of 'spiteful resentment'; and when she did this her voice became full of Violin and there emerged a sound more intense and emotive than I had heard her sing before.

During the next session I led Mary through the Animal Matrix and within a short space of time, she was moving and vocalizing, creating her own animal repertoire. At one point, she spanned her arms like wings and began making flying movements, spinning around and around accompanied by a high pitched screeching sound. Over the next twenty minutes Mary composed an extravagant dance of her voice, rushing like a tornado up and down the Pitch scale, singing and moving, creating a panoply of winged creatures. She became a hot-blooded prehistoric 'ravenasaurus', soaring at top speed across valley and plain, brandishing her beak and bellowing out the cries of hunger. She became a great winged compound of part heron and part stork, perched and poised; she became a screeching pink flamingo, a squawking magpie, a wild black crow and a parrot with the full colour of plumage. As Mary journeyed through the matrix of bird imagery her voice became very loud and extremely powerful; and she became particularly engaged in the transformation back and forth between the stork and the crow. The former she felt symbolized the role of nurse and midwife she had played all her life whilst the crow somehow stood for the 'blackness' and 'anger' that she felt.

Mary now spoke about her memories of being a surrogate mother to her sister and brother and began to reveal her unexpressed resentment, not only towards her mother for dying but also towards her brother and sister for needing care, her own children for 'taking every ounce of energy she had' and towards her husband for falling ill and leaving her 'unprovided for'. During her reportage, Mary happened to say that her sister had always accused her of being spiteful and she had in fact been quite malicious during her own childhood. Furthermore, after the death of her mother she had recurring dreams in which her sister died, releasing Mary from the burden of care-giving. In addition, during the mothering of her own children, she often had sporadic 'spiteful' feelings towards them and she often felt that they kept her from 'living her own life'. However, Mary had repressed all this because it was 'negative and destructive' and 'anyway' she said that she loved her children dearly.

We continued exploring the Animal Matrix, which gave Mary a framework within which to release and explore her sense of repressed spite and resentment. Then as she passed down into Feline-canine Position, her head dropped, her hands gripped tight and she held her posture with her sight line passing down her torso, as though looking through her legs. Then she began to cry. Her voice, which was normally in Flute Timbre, changed to Saxophone Timbre as her voice tube expanded, allowing her emotions to pour forth more vehemently than they ever had before. The Feline-canine Position had caused Mary to experience the weight of her breasts hanging from her chest and this physical sensation had somehow encapsulated and crystallized her feeling of having been 'sucked dry' by her brother, sister, children and husband, leaving her 'shrivelled' and 'empty'. I gave Mary the image of a drought-weary lioness, fatigued with heat, worn and exhausted with well-suckled nipples, prowling through the bush. She sang soporifically, with wide gaping yawns in Saxophone Timbre with a very slow Pitch Fluctuation and lots of Free Air and Violin.

As Mary explored the Feline-canine movements, she seemed to discover a fresh energetic quality and she began to move and vocalize with complete engagement. She hissed and spat and clawed, her voice manifesting extremely fast vibrato as it passed back and forward between Modal Register and Falsetto Register. She concocted a liquid voice made of arsenic and strychnine and there emerged the character of a creature half cat and half crow, with an acidic voice which burns and bleaches with every note. Then, as she rolled over on her back, she sang like a viper, like a boa constrictor. I asked her to decrease the Loudness and make the spite more conniving and ensnaring, like a spider slowly and cautiously spinning a web of death and then as a scorpion quickly and impulsively injecting the poison. The images of insects increased both the quality of spite and the intensity and strength of the voice. Now as we worked, a fresh network of images unfolded in the voice which built up an emotional field composed of a premeditative revenge against an oppressor; and she became a character, half insect and half crow, with a fatal sting that aimed to kill, slowly. Gradually, these emotions and images birthed a voice nearly one-and-a-half octaves higher than when we had started and which sounded calm, strong and self-possessed.

The next time we worked together Mary manifested a voice which combined Violin and Free Air which we both experienced as full of vitality, energy and verve and she began to explore sounds associated with childhood. Her voice gurgled and effervesced with innocence and naïvety and she sang with the freshness and purity of a kitten untouched by trauma. As she sung, Mary's face took on an open and inquisitive smile which I had not seen before.

The Animal Matrix provided a framework in which Mary could explore the shadow side of the good nurse and the good mother, an entirely necessary process for someone who had been prematurely denied her own mother and forced into assuming the role of a good mother herself. Her issues were connected to the age-old archetypal nature of the mother in all her aspects – nurturing and destroying, compassionate and spiteful, bitter and sweet. And through her voice, she reclaimed the sound of the child which had not had the space to be heard before.

Instinct and order

One of our constant tasks as human beings is to balance our instinct with our reason. The burden of this task is the price we pay for having separated ourselves from the animals and endowed ourselves with cognition and consciousness. The balance between instinct and reason is essential if we are to avoid succumbing to the monopoly of either one.

In Greek mythology, the god Dionysus is a fine symbol for the instinctual and spontaneous aspects of art and psyche; while Apollo represents the reasoning components of order. When Apollo is left alone without the subverting and agitating force of Dionysus he becomes pedantic, analytical, formal and uninspired. In therapy, this unenlivened Apollo rears his head in the endless sessions of the 'talking cure' where stories are told and retold and the language of the soul is subjected to analytical paradigms that remain unembodied, unemotive and unexploded. With an Apollonian emphasis, unsuspecting pilgrims are sold the illusion that if only they can comprehend the way their past has moulded the present they will be able to guarantee themselves an alternative future. But healing cannot occur through analysis alone.

When Dionysus is left alone without the guiding parameters of Apollo, he rages out of control and leads those who follow him into self-destruction. In therapy, this untutored Dionysus rears his head in the boundless sessions of pure catharsis where deep breathing leads to the mania of hyperventilation and where tearful passions recreate the tragic theatre of trauma and despair. Some people have the illusion that if they go on pouring out the sediment of their heart they will empty themselves of sorrow and be freed from the aftermath of their own history. In the short term, like all excursions into abandonment, relief is forthcoming. But later, when the cold winds of morning and the blue light of day replace the exhilaration of the night before, the soul is as full as it ever was. Experience is not a liquid quantity that is poured into us; it is a calligraphy that is written upon us. Healing cannot occur through catharsis alone; it must be accompanied by purposeful artistic creativity. And for this we need the formal principles provided by Apollo.

When Apollo and Dionysus work together, then the outpourings of emotion, in the form of eruptive sounds, can be shaped by the creative principles of Apollo to produce a holding place for a history that cannot be unwritten but can be sung to a different tune. Working with precise physical postures and sounds in a choreographic and acoustic matrix of exercises provides the Apollonian order within which the spontaneous and unbridled instincts of Dionysus can roam free.

CHAPTER TEN

Prayers and Prophecies

*How people from all spiritual traditions have used the
voice to contact the soul and why we should do the same*

Songs of the shaman

In many ancient civilizations and early indigenous cultures, administering medicine to the sick was the sacred function of a shaman. A shaman is a complex combination of sorcerer, witch-doctor, spiritual healer, seer, soothsayer, augur, prophet, herbalist, psychotherapist, priest, monk and artist. Shamanism used to be a widespread phenomenon throughout the world until Western allopathic medicine became omnipresent. But shamans can still be found in Siberia, Central Asia, the Malay Peninsula, Alaska, Central America, Papua New Guinea and among the nomadic peoples of the Sahara and the Sudan, as well as among the Aborigines of Australia.

The shaman's way of healing is predicated on the belief that illness always has a spiritual cause. The cure is therefore designed to rid the body and soul of the violating spirits which impede health. The shaman is in many ways an exorcist, often taking the afflicting spirits into his own body and then discharging them in a process of personal catharsis when the patient is cured.

Songs and vocal sounds are always central to this process of shamanic healing. As the shaman flushes the pestilent spirits from the patient they are released in the form of bizarre and unearthly vocal sounds comprising a string of syllables, cries, screams, groans, grumbles and improvised melodies; and the shaman often identifies himself with an animal who bestows a primitive wisdom on the healer. After the cathartic exorcism the shaman discharges the spirits from his own body through a similar dance of vocal release. In many cultures, the shaman also sings special healing songs which are believed to be the lost language of ancient animals and are endowed with a magical healing power. During healing ceremonies the shaman dances into a delirium, singing songs chosen from a repertoire of curative words and melodies and chanting a maniacal and indecipherable language considered to be the tongue of the spirit world.

In many of the northern tribes of American Indians, where shamanic healing has always been central to the medicine kit, part of the cure involves finding the elder of the tribe who knows the exact song that will heal a particular illness. These medicine songs come to certain chosen ones in special prophetic dreams. Only by remembering and guarding the life-long memory of the song can the dreamer protect the tribe from impending destruction by infectious illness. Among the Australian Aboriginal Wurajeri peoples, the process by which a novice becomes a doctor includes having a spiritual guide and companion 'sung into' him by an elder. This singing transmission enables the healing power of the elder to be duplicated in the novice. Meanwhile, the Yamana medicine men of Tierra del Fuego can only be initiated as authentic healers through the act of singing, which activates their shamanic souls.

Many sacred traditions from all quarters of the globe include a belief in the sacred potential of certain vocal sounds to awaken the soul, purify the spirit and invoke divine presence. Unlike Western allopathic medicine, which evolved as a scientific counterpoint to religious ministry, many other Eastern approaches to healing have retained an intimate connection to spiritual belief and practice. For example, the ancient Chinese understanding of our physical and spiritual nature believes in a flow of an energy known as 'chi' through bodily pathways known as meridians. This chi energy is thought to be spiritually and physically beneficial but can also become blocked near a particular nexus, causing the body and soul to suffer disease and unease. It is this paradigm which underpins the healing art of acupuncture and acupressure as well as the discipline of yoga.

In India, the Hindus developed a perception of the soma based on the belief that the human body contains a series of 'energy wheels' known as 'chakras' which are spaced vertically parallel to the spine. Each chakra is connected to a nerve plexus and an endocrine gland and influences the health of vital body organs as well as the health of the spirit. Physical and spiritual health is maintained by ensuring that energy can pass freely up through the chakras from the root to the crown; and the chanting of specific sounds serves to keep the chakras clear for the passage of this energy, awakening the psyche and soma to health. To this end, the Hindus chant repetitively a Sanskrit prayer, known as a mantra.

In Buddhism, meanwhile, there has always been less emphasis on the treatment of bodily disease and a deeper focus on accepting and alleviating suffering through compassionate and mindful behaviour.

In order to achieve this, the Buddhist must seek to quieten the in-cessant inner voices which fill the mind with the appetites of the ego. One of the ways by which the Buddhist achieves this emptying of the mind is through chanting repetitive sounds, of which the most familiar to Western ears is the sound 'om'.

The power of the voice is also central to the Islamic prayer where the muezzin places both hands on his temples and calls the faithful to prayer from the minaret. And within the secret schools of Sufism, which formed the mystical roots of Islam across the Persian and Arabic region from Turkey to Afghanistan, singing was used as a central key to the door of enlightenment.

Sounds of heaven and earth

The roots of the Christian faith are also alive with the power of voice. At the close of communion just before his crucifixion, Jesus sang the *Hallel* with his disciples and their singing voices rang out. The song of the disciples defied death in a prophetic fanfare that was echoed when Jesus defied death through his resurrection. Later the apostle Paul urged those who converted to the path of Jesus to acknowledge their faith through singing. Paul believed that we can be born again into grace through songs of faith as Jesus had the faith to sing moments before his death.

The Judaeo-Christian tradition of giving voice to faith begins in the Old Testament. Moses and his sister, the prophetess Miriam, wor-shipped and praised God in triumphant song during the miraculous parting of the Red Sea as God brought the Israelites into the promised land; women and children joined in a procession of singing to celebrate the victory of David over Goliath; and believers who are filled with the spirit broke into spontaneous ecstatic songs sung in the tongues of unknown languages. When Jesus brings the resounding voice of a New Testament to the world, he inspires the voices of those who follow him; and in the Apocalypse, the throng of believers known as the Brides of Christ sing an oratorio of redemption to the accom-paniment of angels. But, the power of the human voice is nowhere more perfectly illustrated than in the story of Joshua who, after marching round the city a total of thirteen times, commanded the people to shout. And the sound of their voices caused the walls of Jericho to fall down flat.

The human voice as emissary for the spirit of God plays a particu-larly vital role in contemporary Christian worship where the phenom-enon known as glossolalia, or speaking in tongues, occurs. During worship a member of a congregation may become possessed with the spirit and be caused to sing a spontaneous improvisation in a semi-articulate form that has the appearance of a language but does not correspond to any known tongue. This sonorous appearance of the spirit is recorded in the New Testament. Several days after the death of Christ and his ascension to heaven, the disciples were gathered to await the fulfilment of his promise to return. Suddenly, there came from heaven 'a sound as of the rushing of a mighty wind' and there 'appeared unto them tongues parting asunder, like as of fire and it sat on each one of them' and 'they were filled with the Holy Ghost'. So it was that the disciples of Jesus 'began to speak in other tongues as the Spirit gave them utterance'.

From the placid plain chants of the early Christian church to the repetitive toning of *om* by Buddhist monks, from speaking in tongues to Sufi songs, from the sung prophecies of early mystics to the powerful calling of the muezzin, from African invocations to Sanskrit poems, people of all beliefs have shared in the power of the voice to lift the spirits, attain enlightenment and reach the ears of God. Yet it is not necessary to possess a religious conviction in order to find a sense of spiritual peace, for the voice alone is capable of awakening your spirit.

One of the exercises which makes up the system of Voice Movement Therapy is called the Prayer Cycle and I have witnessed the positive healing effect of this exercise on people from diverse spiritual affiliations, including the sceptical and agnostic.

Psychologically, the prayer is made up of three elements: imploring, thanking and questioning. Praying is a time when we can ask for what we need; it enables us to call out to have our thirsts and hungers satiated. When we have been provided with the things for which we implored, praying also enables us to call out in gratitude for our abundance. But when our needs have not been met, praying is also a time for giving voice to our disappointment and bewilderment and enables us to ask why our prayers have not been answered.

These three elements of the prayer are also core components of human experience; we all experience times of imploring; we are all blessed with times of plenty; and we all have periods where our needs seem to fall on deaf ears and we are left questioning why. In Voice Movement Therapy, the prayer is used to give shape and form to these primary human experiences so that we may be healed from the agony of having no means to express our need, our gratitude and our disappointment.

Voice Movement Therapy Exercise
The Prayer Cycle

To begin, create a Spherical Space, stand comfortably in the centre of the sphere and breathe in and out through your mouth with the voice tube in Flute Configuration. Bring your arms horizontally out in front of you and with your palms turned upwards, make the shape of a bowl. Tilt your head back a little and look up to the heavens. Now begin to vocalize, combining the other ingredients of your voice freely to create a vocal prayer and allow the emotional intention which motivates your prayer to move between three core aspects of the prayer: imploring, thanks and questioning. As you vocalize, allow your tongue, lips and jaw to create an original and spontaneous language made up of syllables and words which may not mean anything linguistically but which express the sentiment of your soul. This is called the Standing Prayer (*see* figure 17a).

Now, as you vocalize, bend your knees, implode your chest into a concave arc, move your pelvis towards the ground as you would if you were sitting, tilt your head down and look into the bowl created by the palms of your hands. Now, allow the voice tube to expand and listen to the voice shift into Clarinet Timbre. Because the voice tube is now more expanded, you will probably find that your implorings, gratitudes and questioning are expressed with more passion. Continue combining the other ingredients of the voice freely. Treat your bowl as a metaphor for your sense of abundance. If your bowl is full, use your voice to call in thanks; if your bowl is empty, use your voice to implore or to question with disappointment. This is called the Sitting Prayer (*see* figure 17b).

Now, as you vocalize, take your body down and sit on your haunches moving the torso up and down between a horizontal position laying across your thighs and a vertical position, lifting your prayer bowl up from the floor and down again – as though you were on a prayer mat. Now allow the voice tube to expand to maximum dimensions and listen to the voice shift into Saxophone Timbre. Because the voice

Voice Movement Therapy Exercise

tube is now fully expanded, you will probably find that your implorings, gratitudes and questioning are expressed with great power. Continue to focus on your bowl and contemplate where in your life your bowl is full and where it is empty, giving vocal expression to your realizations. This is called the Kneeling Prayer (*see* figure 17c).

Now, come back into the Sitting Prayer, allowing the voice to return to Clarinet Timbre; and then return back to the Standing Prayer, allowing the voice to shift back into Flute Timbre. This completes the Prayer Cycle.

a) The Standing Prayer

b) The Sitting Prayer

a) The Kneeling Prayer

Figure 17 **The Prayer Cycle**

The prayer chair

Jonathan was mentally handicapped, a term which descends from a terminological lineage which has included 'imbecile', 'stupid', 'retarded' and 'backward'. Jonathan had been in a residential home for thirty years and in that time, only the name used to describe his condition had changed. He was thirty-eight years old, had deep green piercing eyes, gigantic teeth and hands like plates. The first time I saw him he was sitting in a circle in the common room of his home with thirty-seven men and women ranging in age from twenty-two to sixty-one, who had gathered obediently to take part in a 'voice workshop'.

Jonathan had been classified 'non verbal' but he was certainly highly vocal; his voice sporadically emitted a stream of guttural sounds accompanied by an undulating and wave-like dance of his arms, as though he was saying goodbye to a departing loved one knowing she will never be seen again. Jonathan had been abandoned at the age of six; his parents were still alive but had not visited him for twenty-three years. The staff at the centre thought his sporadic vocal emissions to be harmless but meaningless.

I was once travelling in Turkey during the festival of Ramadan. It was a hot and dusty evening and the town was deserted. As I turned a corner to buy some water, I heard a sound which grabbed my attention: a moaning, pleading, yearning sound which had a pump-like pulse to it. I could not understand the words uttered, and I do not know even if they were words. The sound was neither despairing nor euphoric, it was neither melodic nor was it lacking in musical form; it was, in essence, spiritual.

I retraced my steps a little way and took upon myself the audacity to peer in through a hole in the blinds of a small house, where I saw a man kneeling with tears in his eyes and beads in his hands. I looked only for a moment; then I turned and listened once more. At this point my entire interpretative faculties went into overdrive in an attempt to classify and comprehend this sound.

Was he crying? Was he singing? Was he praying? And the movements I saw him make with his arms? Were they the spontaneous expression of uncontrollable grief? Or were they the orderly gestural accompaniment to worship?

I could not answer any of these questions but could only imagine that the ambiguity and unclassifiable nature of his vocal dance was somehow an important part of why it moved me so much.

In the centre for mentally handicapped adults we went around the circle one by one, each member calling out a sound which the group called back. When it came to Jonathan's turn, something happened that caused me to experience a deep sense of awe. He called out a sound which I had not heard since the time I had stood on that hot dusty street corner in Turkey; and I thought only one thing. If we had taken Jonathan to Turkey and placed him in a room with blinded windows and asked him to call out his sound, passers-by may have asked all kinds of questions. Is he praying? Is he chanting? Is he singing? But they would not for a moment have thought to ask: is he handicapped?

Jonathan's sound was not handicapped. It was full of religiosity, yearning, needing, pleading and worship. It was also full of music. However, because the linguistic content of Jonathan's day-to-day acoustic emissions were not understandable, 'the baby had been thrown out with the bath water' and his entire vocal faculty had been disqualified and rendered insignificant.

In most parts of Europe, singing teachers teach with what they consider to be the indispensable aid of the piano; any vocal sounds made by the student which do not correspond to the black or the white notes are considered unmusical. Western classical music is black and white.

It only takes fifteen minutes in Turkey, Egypt, Argentina, India or Bali to discover how limited this view of music is. In those countries whose musical traditions have been unaffected by the black and white philosophy they bend notes in continual defiance of a single Pitch. This is one of the qualities which Jonathan's voice had in common with the man I had heard in Turkey. Jonathan's sounds were not black and white; nor were they meaningless.

I asked Jonathan to wheel himself into the centre of the circle and asked him to sing with me. As he did, I choreographed the repetitive and involuntary movements of his arms which always accompanied his vocalization into a dance of praying. I began by singing very quietly in such a way as to create the mood and image of a Turkish prayer. I asked Jonathan to sing with me and to develop the movements of his arms into a dance of praying, bending down from the waist in his wheelchair as though kneeling.

It was clear that the wheelchair was restricting him so we helped him out of the chair and into a comfortable kneeling position on the floor. I knelt behind him and held him around the waist with my cheek resting in the small of his back. Together we arose and descended as though in prayer and chanted together in an improvisation of wavering and undulating notes which turned the common room into a sacred space, a temple, a mosque, a synagogue, a church.

I kept repeating Jonathan's sounds back to him with exact replication – except for one thing. Whereas Jonathan sang in Flute Timbre, I sang back to him in Saxophone Timbre. Eventually, he was able to copy me exactly and his voice tube lengthened and expanded. With this, he lost a certain strain and tension in his voice and its tonal range increased considerably.

After some time, Jonathan became quite excited and enthused by the process, and this was expressed vocally in little spasmodic peeping noises in Falsetto Register. I began to mirror these sounds until our musical improvisation gradually transformed into a rhythmical and semi-operatic melody with a xylophone-type quality. In order to ease out the Falsetto sounds, I massaged and patted his back, and eventually I was playing his body like a drum. Each time I struck a part of his back, a clear note would emerge. These notes became stronger, clearer and longer as time went on and it finally became apparent that not only did Jonathan have an awe-inspiring capacity to work in lower pitches, he also had a wonderful upper range akin to a choir boy's. By the end of our session, Jonathan's voice was dancing free and his peers were clapping and smiling with glee as they witnessed the soul of their fellow fill the air.

Swallowing pride

I have worked with many people like Jonathan and sometimes, when faced with those who have no opportunity to change their social circumstances, it is the sharing of a prayer that points the way ahead and enables those like Jonathan to uncover their soul, often bringing shame on those who limit such people with labels like 'non-verbal' and 'handicapped'. We all have a handicapped part, a part that limps and strains and falters in the face of the most simple tasks. Yet we all have a voice which remains free from impediment; and this voice must be heard.

Just because someone cannot speak does not mean that their voice is meaningless; it means that we must have the humility to learn their language and converse in their tongue. Even music therapists who have trained to apply their musicianship to a healing end have difficulty in letting go of formality and allowing their voice to roam free in unison with those whose voices are primal and inarticulate. But for those who want to be vocal healers it is essential. Pride can only be our prison. We must listen to those like Jonathan and learn from their lack of inhibition; for we have as much to borrow from them as they do from us.

PART FOUR

The Political Voice

Sounding Sensual

*Why the voice is a sex organ and how it is used to
attract and seduce*

Love talk

When we fall in love we do so based on what we see and what we hear
and though 'love at first sight' is a more familiar cliché than 'love at
first hearing', the voice is crucial in the process of attraction and
seduction. A beautiful voice has the power to enchant whilst an ugly
voice repels.

In the French story of Cyrano de Bergerac, Cyrano is madly in love
with a beautiful woman called Roxanne but he is convinced that his
love is in vain due to his having an excessively long nose. Meanwhile,
a young attractive man named Christian falls in love with the same
woman but does not know how to enchant her with his words. So,
Cyrano pours out words of love for Roxanne from his heart and gives
them to the young man. But in the end, the young woman discovers
that the words which have enchanted her come from Cyrano, and she
falls in love with him despite his nose.

Cyrano de Bergerac is one of many stories which remind us of the
important role played by the voice of the heart in the expression of
love. When we are young and in the company of our first love, words
seem to desert us as we struggle to create a rapport. Even as adults, we
can spend hours pondering what we should say to someone whom
we secretly desire. Then, when it seems that feelings are mutual,
words pour from our mouths and we relax into endless conversations
which we voice with the ease of making love. There are many clichés
and stereotypes of the sexy voice: the breathy, husky voice of a woman
and the deep, gravelly voice of a man; and many singers have deliberately cultivated a voice which communicates a sexual image, arousing
the erotic susceptibility of listeners and enticing an audience into
feelings of adoration that compare to those often felt towards a lover.

The hormonal voice

The fact that voice is so crucial in the game of love is understandable given that the voice is itself a sex organ. The vocal cords are connected to the thyroid cartilage, an important part of the endocrine system which distributes hormones throughout the body. A healthy endocrine system and the timely release of hormones is essential for the development of gender characteristics such as fertility. For example, during puberty, the testicles release hormones which travel around the endocrine circuit of glands, causing the boy's thyroid cartilage and larynx to shift in position. This drop of the larynx slackens the vocal cords and consequently lowers the Pitch range of the boy's voice.

During the Baroque and Renaissance of seventeenth- and eighteenth-century Europe, many young boys were castrated before puberty to prevent this change from occurring. When these boys grew to manhood, they retained a child-like high-pitched voice and became known as castrati. These singers were admired and sought after for their angelic and androgynous quality, for they had voices as high as any woman could sing but the faces and bodies of men. The most renowned castrato was Farinelli, who was employed by the Queen of Spain to cure her husband of madness by singing sweetly to his troubled mind; but the Queen of Spain was not alone in believing that the castrato's voice was somehow imbued with a magical and healing power. As well as singing in concerts and in the courts, castrati were also employed by the Vatican, who needed high voices but did not allow women to sing. However, Pope Leo XIII banned castrati from the church towards the end of the eighteenth century and they began to disappear as the practice of castration became less popular.

The hormonal secretions of the endocrine system also affect a woman's voice, particularly during menstruation, pregnancy and menopause, all of which can be accompanied by changes in the quality of the voice. In fact, many lead opera singers who have to sing large demanding roles now demand a contract which relieves them from having to perform during menstruation.

Because the quality of the voice depends, in part, upon the chemical processes of the endocrine system, any hormonal transformation can potentially cause a change in vocal tonal colour. Furthermore, because hormonal alterations can occur as a result of our emotional reaction to events and circumstances, anything which affects the psyche can influence our hormonal balance which in turn can affect the voice.

Animus and anima

Every man has a feminine dimension, known as his 'anima' and every woman has a male side, known as her 'animus'; and the presence of the other gender can be contacted and expressed through the voice. Accepting qualities normally associated with 'the other sex' is often a difficult process and we resist it more adamantly the greater we feel the need to stress the characteristics of our given gender.

Voice Movement Therapy Exercise

The Loving Voice

Begin by singing a Pitch in the middle of your range. See if you can sing the note first in Modal Register and then again in Falsetto Register.

Now rise in Pitch and sing up and down your upper range in Falsetto Register. As you sing, reflect upon the voice of your mother. Let the timbral quality of your mother's voice linger in your mind's ear and, as you sing, try to combine the ingredients of your voice to produce a sound which emulates the voice of your mother.

As you sing with your mother in mind, notice your feelings and sensations and reflect upon the connections between your own masculine and feminine qualities and those of your mother.

Now descend in Pitch and sing up and down your lower range in Modal Register. As you sing, reflect upon the voice of your father. Let the timbral quality of your father's voice linger in your mind's ear and, as you sing, try to combine the ingredients of your voice to produce a sound which emulates the voice of your father.

As you sing with your father in mind, notice your feelings and sensations and reflect upon the connections between your own masculine and feminine qualities and those of your father.

Now sing up and down your complete range and consider the person whom you have loved most intimately in your adult life. Let love pour out through your voice. As you sing, compare the feelings of love which you have for your intimate partner with those you have for your mother and father. Linger too in the places where you feel an absence of love.

Allow words of love, and words which express an absence of love, to come to you and then, when you have finished vocalizing, write them down. Now sing your song of love, giving it a melody by amplifying the prosody of your speaking voice.

Because we associate high-pitched voices in Falsetto Register with a female voice, for a man to produce such a voice requires him to rise above his one-sided masculinity and reunite his soul with the dormant anima. Because the high voice has its roots in the pre-pubescent stage of our development, it is also naturally associated with the youthful essence within us and for a man to access this voice he must also awaken the realm of infancy and give voice to the inner child. But because most of us first hear such a high voice emerge from the mouth of the mother, many men find that vocalizing in the higher range reactivates feelings towards their own mother as well as awakening their own maternal instincts.

Conversely, for a woman to touch the depths of the low voice, she must transcend her notions of femininity and unite her soul with the dormant animus. Because most of us first hear such a deep voice come from the mouth of the father, many women find that vocalizing in the lower range reactivates feelings towards their father as well as awakening their own paternal instincts. In addition, when we sing low sounds there is a sense of descending low into the body and a feeling that the sound is excavated from the abdomen. Paradoxically, for a woman this naturally vivifies feelings and sensations connected to the womb and many women describe their deep voice as liquid blood, reminding them of their fertility and their ability to initiate their own psychological rebirth.

Sally sings for love

I once worked with a young woman who had been born prematurely. Her first glance at the world was through the confining walls of a plastic incubator. But that was not all. During the period when most children are beginning to talk, Sally was very sick and spent the majority of her second and third years in and out of a hospital crib.

Apparently her mother was an anxious woman who, after Sally's birth, lived with the knowledge that her baby might die. Throughout Sally's life, her mother had been over-protective, as though she never quite recovered from the possibility of losing her daughter. As a result, Sally had entered adult life with little worldly wisdom. She was extremely shy, lacking in self-confidence and described herself as very quiet.

She worked as a filing clerk in a large law firm. She was reasonably happy but felt that people saw her as insignificant. Her speaking voice was quiet and full of Free Air and she had a habitual gesture of brushing the fringe of her hair out of her eyes and across her forehead.

Sally found entering conversations very difficult. She said that when a group of people were talking together, she felt as though she could wait for ever for a door to open and let her in. Once she found her way through the door, however, she was able to talk freely, so long as the nature of the conversation was not competitive or argumentative. I asked Sally what she would change about herself if she could. She replied instantly that she would like to find a man whom she could love and who would love her in return; and she said that in order to do this she felt she needed to be more able to express her strength and aggression.

When I first asked Sally to make a long open sound, she sang a note which was, to my ears, melancholic, romantic and sombre. Her voice was high in Pitch with lots of Free Air, in Falsetto Register and Clarinet Timbre with just a smattering of Violin. I asked her to journey around her voice making playful childlike sounds. She sang beautiful light notes on 'do bee doo tum be go la woo'. She giggled and remarked on how simple and yet how enjoyable it felt to do this. As I listened to Sally sing, it aroused in me the image of Audrey Hepburn or Grace Kelly standing on a bridge in the arms of a chivalrous gentleman. I asked Sally to allow the notes to wander up and down and suggested that she sing with an air of romance. As her voice began weaving gently and graciously a little higher and a little lower, Sally began to weep.

Sally had never had a relationship with a man, although she was twenty-six years old. She wanted love, the love of a man. She desired to contact her strength and aggression because she believed this would prevent her from being ignored and enable her to seek a relationship with confidence. But neither strength nor aggression was the goal. Love was.

As I knew that Sally loved to listen to music, I asked her to find some love songs before the next session and to learn the one which moved her the most. She arrived a week later with a piece of paper upon which were inscribed the words of 'The Way We Were'. As she sang this song I envisioned a young couple waltzing along a pier or a promenade accompanied by the lapping waves and a distant accordion. When I told her this, she smiled and recalled a time when her father had taken her to the seaside without her mother or her brother. In the evening, before returning home, her father had sat with her on the pier and he had taught her a song about a lonesome sailor. Sally had inherited her musical inclination from her father who had loved to sing and played the accordion.

I now asked Sally to sing 'The Way We Were' a second time, imagining that she was once again on the pier singing to her father. She did this exquisitely; and as she sang, I noticed that the hand which usually brushed her fringe across her forehead was now stroking her upper chest, in the region of her heart. This choreographic sweeping movement, which had drawn my attention from the beginning, seemed to take on more depth now that her hand was upon her heart rather than her brow. But before Sally reached the end of the song she stopped, began to cry and sob violently and then, in an instant, her sorrow turned to rage and she began yelling 'It isn't fair' over and over again.

Her mother had not only protected Sally from the outside world, but also from her father; her mother had perceived him as too coarse, crude and altogether a bad influence. Her parents divorced when Sally was thirteen and her mother made it extremely difficult for her daughter to visit her father. She missed him terribly. When Sally was nineteen, her father died suddenly in a boating accident.

Sally had not felt threatened by her father at all. In fact she remembered him as affectionate, warm and understanding. Meanwhile, Sally could not remember ever being cuddled or kissed, held or sang to by her mother. She had gone from the womb to a plastic incubator and from the incubator to the cool and mechanical arms of her anxious mother.

I sat quietly but with my heart in full attendance while Sally yelled and screamed and raged. She seemed to be releasing so much previously unexpressed emotion. She felt so incensed at her mother for extinguishing the relationship that she had had with her father – a rage intensified by the fact that the man was now dead and it was all too late. Her heart was drenched in grief for the father she almost had.

The sounds which Sally made were highly intense; her face was red, her eyes gleamed with the glare of a panther, her breathing was deep as a barrel and the walls shook with the volume of her voice. I wondered if anyone had been there for Sally in a way which permitted her to release such sound before.

When Sally eventually settled and we began talking, I pointed out that her voice had, during her rage, taken on a robust and retaliatory quality and I helped Sally rediscover this sound when we worked together the following week. This new voice was extremely loud, low in Pitch, in Saxophone Timbre and Modal Register and thundered with an extremely fast Pitch Fluctuation. Leading Sally down the scale, she found an altogether different sound to the graceful voice of the young woman in love. This sound was ravenous, dark and enfolding. It was also low down in the range of a classical baritone as it flowed out of her like a deep dark river. I also noticed that Sally had replaced the stroking of her heart with a new dance. Both hands were now rubbing her belly in a circular motion as though this new sound somehow emerged from there.

The next time we worked Sally practised moving back and forth between the two sounds which she had discovered: the light romantic sound of love and the weighted, deep sound of rage. She slipped easily between the two and as she did this, I asked her to develop her hand-dance by touching her chest and then her belly. What had at first been a nervous repetitive gesture of brushing her fringe out of her eyes now took on balletic eloquence and proportion. As she sang in the light voice, she ran her palm over her chest and extended her arm outwards as though taking her heart upon her sleeve and offering love to her suitor. When she sang in the weighted voice, she caressed her belly as though dammed up behind the walls of her abdomen was a powerful flood of determination.

The two distinct voices were highly significant for Sally. The light, high voice expressed a number of things. It was the voice of the little girl who had been denied the man she first loved, her father, who was both sailor and singer. But this was also the voice of a romantic young woman who had so much love to give and who was searching for a man to love her and not leave her as her father had done. Meanwhile, her low baritone voice encapsulated the rage against her mother; she felt her mother had suffocated her. However, it also expressed the deep strength she had, a strength which she felt in her belly. This was not the strength of anger or aggression, it was not the voice of attack or revenge. This was a voice which expressed the strength inherent in the virtues of patience, perseverance and faithfulness.

When I saw Sally for our next session she told me that our work together had prompted her to visit her mother. She had felt that she somehow wanted to get beneath the rage and disappointment and find some warmth in the relationship.

To Sally's amazement, her mother disclosed that a year before Sally's birth she had lost her first baby to an hereditary illness at only eight months old. From that point on, there had been no affection between Sally's mother and father. Sally's father had begun drinking and had, in her mother's words, 'closed down and shut off'. From this conversation, Sally learned what her mother had endured and how her mother had lived with the fear of losing her second child while trying to sustain a marriage after the lights had gone out.

During the session, we worked on her voice, aiming to bring together the light romantic sound and heavy dark sound into a single quality. At the end, Sally said that she felt she had discovered the real sadness: that her mother and father could not have both taken her to the seaside, that her father never again sang to his wife after the death of his first born, that she only ever saw her mother's cool disposition without knowing how it had come to be.

Some weeks later, when we finished our work together, Sally said that she had noticed herself both giving and receiving more warmth and affection at work. She found this strange as she had originally imagined that she needed to express herself more aggressively. Yet she was now actually extending her heart to her colleagues in a way that was both vulnerable yet strong. In return, her professional associates were smiling at her, asking if she was well, looking at her straight in the eye. Sally said she felt as though she was thawing out after a big chill.

I heard from Sally six months after her last session. She had fallen in love. I never did hear what happened, but whatever the outcome I like to imagine that Sally and her man made it to the seaside and found time to stand upon the pier and sing to the ocean.

We shall be released

Sally had spent a long time in prison. The prison of the incubator, the prison of the hospital crib, the prison of isolation from the father who she had loved, the prison of a lonely life without affection. But most of all, like many of us, Sally was imprisoned by language. Speech was not her friend, it did not represent her inner experience to the outside world. When she spoke, people saw only little Sally, insignificant Sally, the cool young clerk who stood back from affectionate contact.

Sally uncovered some of her deepest emotions; she gained some crucial insights into her family relationships; but above all she transformed herself from feeling shy and reticent without the propensity to give and receive affection, to feeling open-hearted and connected to the soul and spirit of others. But this journey was facilitated not by talking but by singing, by sound-making, by vocalizing.

The act of singing takes us back to an earlier time, when our emotions were instantly available, when we wore our hearts on our sleeves, our tears on our cheeks and our smiles on our faces. Singing reminds us of the time when we sounded out our emotions the moment they made themselves known. We all need the opportunity to experience this again. For part of the loneliness which Sally felt is the loneliness that each one of us is likely to feel. It is a loneliness which stems from the knowledge that we may never find spoken words to express the fruits which lie hidden in the corners and crevasses of our soul.

Though Sally's story is unique and though each one of us has a song to sing which echoes for us alone, we also share in common many of the fruits which are to be found beneath language in the unspeakable arena of our being. These fruits, which are both bitter and sweet, unite us all; and they must be voiced. For if they are not, we may never come to know the deep capacity for feeling that we have; and we may never be fully heard by others in the world who share those feelings with us. As a consequence, all the blessed qualities which cannot be spoken but that make us human may, for want of light, shrivel up and die. In order to prevent that from happening, we must investigate the nature of these fruits, the things which cannot be spoken but must be voiced.

CHAPTER TWELVE

Noises from the Battlefield

*How those with power have misused the voice as a
weapon of destruction and how those who have been
wounded can recover the sounds of victory*

The girl with mousy hair

In every classroom, in every school, buried somewhere in the middle
row, there sits the quiet child. She makes no trouble, asks few questions and makes little noise. To her classmates she is the girl with the
mousy hair and glasses, noticeable only because she seems to be
shrouded in a sphere of silence. In fact, she could be mistaken for a
mute if she were not heard in a corner of the playground speaking
softly to the other timid children who are her compatriots in secret.
What makes some children especially quiet while all around them
others play loudly?

To understand the timid and the meek, whose voices are soft and
easily drowned by the cacophony of the crowd, it is useful to examine
the extreme example of voicelessness: mutism. Mutism comes from
the Latin *mutos* meaning silent and the person suffering from mutism is
literally struck dumb. Total mutism is quite rare, but when it does
occur its roots are nearly always psychological. The vocal cords can
vibrate, the mouth can articulate and the mind is awash with complex
thoughts and deep feelings. But between the conception and the
sound, between the emotion and word falls a shadow of silence:
the mute is dumb-struck. Though total mutism is quite rare, elective
mutism is relatively common and is a condition of intermittent silence
where a child is perfectly fluent in speech in some circumstances yet
seemingly dumb in others. Some children may go mute at school but
speak clearly at home. Other children may go mute only when in the
presence of doctors and nurses, or when left alone with a stranger, or
when in a large group.

Speech therapists and psychologists working with electively mute
children have discovered that many of these young people are guarding a secret which they are afraid of betraying. Rather than risk the
hidden knowledge slipping out amidst a trail of harmless words, they

close down altogether until they are back in the safe company of those with whom they share the secret.

Silent secrets

Jane was a classic example of a child who kept quiet to avoid spilling the beans. She lived in a large household with her four older sisters and brothers, her parents and her grandparents. Shortly after Jane's birth her mother suffered post-natal depression which developed into a mental illness characterized by irrational and bizarre behaviour, radical changes of mood and vitriolic verbal abuse directed at the grandparents.

When Jane was old enough to ask her grandmother what was wrong with her mummy, she was told: 'Mummy got sick trying to push you out of her tummy and used herself all up trying to look after you.' Understandably, Jane blamed herself for her mother's illness and when I asked her if she felt it was her fault that her mother became mentally ill, Jane replied: 'Well, of course, if I hadn't come along she would be all right.'

When Jane was old enough to begin playing with other children at their homes, her father instructed her to 'never utter a word' about her mother's illness. When Jane began school, these instructions were repeated with greater vehemence when her grandmother told her: 'When you are at school you make sure you say nothing about your mother.' For a young child this amounts to saying nothing at all. For what child can talk without referring to the most significant person in their life? In Jane's case, she did the only thing that could guarantee her ability to satisfy her grandmother's instructions. She said nothing at all when at school. Not a word. She spoke to her friends on her block but with decreasing fluency, until her speech degenerated into single word answers. Eventually she spoke only between the walls of her own house.

Mental illness in the family creates an awful stigma and causes a lot of shame; and the relatives of the sick person can spend as much energy disguising and camouflaging it as they can seeking to heal it. Mental illness also attracts a spectrum of descriptions from the inane to the horrific. The person suffering a mental illness is having a 'nervous breakdown'; they are 'cracking up' or 'falling apart'; they have a 'screw loose', have 'lost their marbles' and gone 'over the edge'. They are mad, insane and demented. These abominable words make it very difficult for a family to discuss the psychological troubles of a loved one and can leave parents bereft of knowing what to say to the children. The so-called professional language of psychiatry is no better and has barely changed since the days of asylums and strait-jackets. Labels like 'senile dementia', 'schizophrenia' and 'manic depression' are blanket terms used to cover such a wide spectrum of individual problems that two people with the same diagnoses may have absolutely nothing in common. It is hard to speak of mental suffering when we lack a compassionate vocabulary for psychological problems. Because of the stigma surrounding mental illness, which is made worse by the language many people use to describe it, the priority of many families is to keep the news from spreading. For the children, this means staying loyal to a code of secrets and lies and avoiding any reference to the psychological difficulties within the family when in public.

Death's whisper

Another subject which a family can find difficult to speak of is death. Death is a skeleton in everyone's cupboard. It lurks with inevitable certainty and yet we talk little of it as though somehow, by leaving it unspoken, we can stave off its coming. When we do speak of death it is often dressed in fear, insecurity and unease. And when our children ask us to give death a name and a face, a rhyme and a reason, we are often quite literally lost for words. The way we present death to children shapes their understanding of what it means to live. If children are offered an explanation that is both truthful yet hopeful, they can grow to accept the only sure event that each of us is guaranteed to encounter. But if we describe death as a finality without a future or if we pretend it does not in some way represent an end, the child can only be troubled, confused and bewildered.

One of the reasons that death can be so difficult to explain is that it is a subject which makes us expose and declare our fundamental spiritual beliefs. For the family with a strong religious foundation, this is hard enough. But for parents whose spiritual life is underdeveloped or unconsidered, knowing what to say to a grief-ridden child when a family member dies is a serious problem. In extreme cases, parents do manage to avoid admitting to the child that a death has occurred and instead they pretend that the deceased family member has temporarily taken a journey and will eventually return.

When one of my clients called John was five years old, his older brother died in a road accident. John did not see the body and did not attend the funeral. When he asked his parents where his brother was, they told him that he had gone away to a special school because he was so clever. John repeatedly asked when they could visit his brother but was answered with false promises and excuses. Like Jane, John was told 'not to breathe a word' about his brother at school, because the other children would be jealous. Like Jane, John became mute for eight months. He would not talk to teachers, to friends or to doctors. He would talk only to relatives.

Both Jane and John were silenced by their loyalty. Rather than risk breaking the family code of privacy, they stopped speaking altogether.

Loyalty is probably the child's most developed instinct; it easily matches the maternal instinct of protection. Even children who are abused by one of their parents will display a loyalty to the family as though by instinct. No matter how harsh, how confusing, how unfair and how destructive, the family is the child's first and last bastion. Children will wage war against the world at large with lies, with protest, with cleverly constructed cover-up stories and if necessary, with complete and utter silence, rather than betray the hand that feeds – even if that hand also threatens.

John and Jane are extreme cases and not all children who guard a family secret become electively mute. But many children become caught in a web of conflict and confusion about what they should and should not say and suffer a milder form of voicelessness called phonophobia.

Phonophobia is literally a fear of voicing and the phonophobic child, though capable of speaking up and speaking out, does so under great duress, terrified that she may say the wrong thing. Beneath this phobia is often a worry that in speaking out they will betray the code of the family and make private knowledge public news. Often children carry this phonophobic condition through into adulthood when they appear as shy, reticent and uncertain of their words. But although phonophobic people seem quiet on the outside, their inner world is often an orchestra of sound. During conversation, their thoughts and feelings swirl round and round in their head like a barrel organ. They know what they think and what they feel; they have an opinion and an elaborate perspective. But between the mind and the throat there is an iron door through which nothing can escape. The phonophobic smiles sweetly and says a simple and agreeable 'ah ah'.

When John and Jane came to work with me they were in their early forties and the mutism of their childhood was far behind them. But they both came seeking help because they felt terribly blocked in their ability to speak out.

Voice Movement Therapy Exercise

The Unspeakable Song

Create a private Spherical Space and sit comfortably.
Reflect upon the things that you consider to be
'unspeakable'. Let these things cross your mind in the form
of images and begin to vocalize the feelings that arise in you.

Then, begin to allow words to be sung and create an
improvised song which expresses some of what you
consider to be unspeakable.

Finally, reflect upon how you feel now you have vocalized
part of your unspeakable self.

Breaking the silence

For those such as John and Jane, speaking remains a burdensome task
and it is difficult for them to experience healing through a form of
therapy founded upon talking. The habit of rendering highly charged
subjects unspeakable is formed when young and becomes entrenched;
and eventually it may seem as though there are simply no words for
certain sensations and experiences.

Using the vocal instrument without words gives phonophobic
people the opportunity to voice without speaking, to express without
naming, to formulate without articulating. Sound rescues the subjects
that have been identified as taboo and releases them from confinement.
Often those such as John and Jane break into incredibly intense
sounds during Voice Movement Therapy and with such sounds comes
a sense of release – like being relieved of the pressure of having to keep
a secret. Yet not a word is spoken. In time, the phonophobic begins to
realize that making a lot of noise is not bad or destructive but good and
constructive. Then, and only then, they may be able to put words to
their greatest fear.

Understanding the healing voice means being sensitive to the subtle
harmonic overtones which exist in spaces between words, underneath
words and above words. Only a small fraction of our soul is speakable;
and many adults have been robbed of the capacity to talk freely about
that fraction. We all live in varying shades of silence where the act of
speaking poorly approximates what our soul wants to say. When all is
said and done, a sound is worth a thousand words.

CHAPTER THIRTEEN

The Song of the Mermaid

*How the wisdom of ancient tales echoes with sound
the song of the sirens*

Breaking the silence

For most people, the process of becoming an adult is a process of becoming increasingly silenced. We come into the world singing our heart out. Then along comes language and chains the soul to the word and leaves the greater part of our self unheard, unvoiced and unsung. Each of us has been silenced to some degree: by family, by teachers, by friends, by expectations, by lovers, by enemies and by the way of the world.

Because so many of us have had our voice stifled, a large part of our journey towards self-discovery, self-empowerment and soulful liberation involves the emancipation of our voice and the unleashing of our self in sound. To rediscover the voice is to rediscover our soul.

The central place that the human voice occupies on the canvas of the human psyche is symbolized in a number of myths, tales and legends. Among the most significant is the story of Echo and Narcissus from Greek myth, the European fairytale 'The Little Mermaid', the story of 'Bluebeard's Castle' and the story of the Sirens, also from Greek myth.

Dangerous duets

The codes and constrictions surrounding the way we experience our growing voice within the original family unit influences the way we vocalize when we create intimate adult relationships and form families of our own. A close adult relationship soon creates its own code of vocal conduct and the rules of our nuptial rapport are often made unconsciously as both partners bring into the relationship remnants of the values which they have been taught. Unfortunately, it is too common for one party to consciously or unconsciously give up the full range of their voice in return for harmony. One person often becomes the resonating vessel which reverberates and echoes the opinions, drives, needs and expressions of the other; and in the process they lose the individual tone of their own voice. This is exemplified clearly in the myth of Echo and Narcissus.

In Greek mythology Echo was a mountain Nymph who helped Zeus – supreme ruler of mortals and gods – to have yet another secret love affair by keeping his wife Hera distracted with idle chatter whilst he was away. So with the incessant chatter of her voice, Echo engaged Hera in constant rapport about everything and nothing. However, when Hera discovered how she had been deceived, she punished Echo by making her unable to speak except to repeat the last words of someone else's speech. So it was that Echo's speaking voice, which had been her spell, her talent and her proclivity, became her handicap. Then, to make matters worse, she fell foolishly in love with Narcissus.

Narcissus was a beautiful youth who refused love from the many hundreds of Nymphs who fell at his feet, including Echo; for Narcissus could love no one. Then, one day Narcissus caught sight of his face mirrored in a pool of water and fell in love with his own reflection. Unable to grasp what he saw, Narcissus pined away and died for love of himself. In the aftermath of his death Echo wilted and withered away in mourning of the love she never had until all that remained of her was her voice.

Echo and Narcissus make a fatal and cataclysmic pair which epitomizes many unfortunate relationships: a man in love with his own reflection and a woman who can do nothing but reflect the voice of the man she loves. As his identity thrives and excels so she loses all sense of self, other than to act as his servile supporter.

Narcissus and Echo are in many ways opposites. He is alive with his own confidence to the point of an over-bearing self-indulgence that precludes him from loving anyone else but himself. She is so transfixed and revering of another in her desperate attempt to be loved that she has no original words to utter and no voice that is truly her own. These opposites reflect the two different experiences which people have of their early life. Some are encouraged to believe in themselves, to have faith in their unique originality and to trust that they are worthy of love. In healthy proportion this can enable us to grow into self-assured human beings with the strength to charter the unfamiliar waters of life with verve and vitality. But when we are encouraged to dwell too long on the beauty of our own character we can become conceited and supercilious, with no room in our lives for the heart and soul of another. Meanwhile, others never benefit from being encouraged to indulge in the splendour of their own identity. They are taught to serve and endow others with greater knowledge, greater ability and greater beauty than themselves. In healthy proportion this can help us to grow into empathetic human beings with the compassion to consider the lives of others with the same loving regard that we would wish for ourselves. But when we are encouraged to stretch our own benevolence and altruism to a point which requires the sacrifice of our own right to self-love, then we can become faceless and voiceless, without sufficient belief in ourselves to be able to offer any genuine love to another. Then all we can do is echo the sound of what we hear in our desperate attempt to have and to hold. Between Echo and Narcissus there is a middle road which combines the love of oneself with the love of another, enabling a relationship that fosters the unison and discord, the harmony and cacophony of two individual voices which create the music of a genuine duet.

The little mermaid

It is, in my experience, often the woman in a relationship or marriage who struggles the hardest to keep her voice alive. Indeed, many women seem to pay the price of their voice in return for the man they love, playing into the web of misogyny that prefers a woman to be modest of tongue. Such a sacrifice is immortalized in the fairytale 'The Little Mermaid'. This tale resonates so exquisitely with anybody seeking to reclaim their voice that it is worth telling in full.

The Little Mermaid was the youngest of six mermaids who lived with their father at the bottom of the ocean. As children they were not permitted to go up to the surface of the waves; but on their fifteenth birthday they were free to swim wherever they pleased. So when it came to the Little Mermaid's fifteenth year she travelled upwards, swam to a ship and peered in through one of the portholes where she saw a beautiful Prince whom she fell in love with at first sight. But then a storm grew and tossed the ship from side to side, tearing down its masts and wrecking its bows. The whole crew were thrown into the ocean and the Prince choked and spat and passed into a deep sleep. So the Little Mermaid carried the Prince to the shore and then swam back out to sea where she watched until a beautiful young woman came, awoke the Prince and took him to safety.

The Little Mermaid returned to the bottom of the ocean but spent her days in mourning, longing to be rid of her fish's tail and to have two legs so she might enter the world of the land and win the love of the Prince she had saved from death but who had never set eyes on her.

So, the Little Mermaid went to the Sea Witch who said: 'I know what you want. It is stupid of you, for it will bring you grief, but you shall have your way, my pretty Princess. You want to get rid of your fishtail and to have two legs instead, like those the people of the earth walk with, so that the young Prince might fall in love with you. Very well, I will prepare a potion for you; and when you drink it your tail will shrivel up and become legs. But it will hurt you. It will seem as if you have been cut with a sharp sword. You will have a graceful walk and no dancer will be able to move as lightly as you. But every step you take will be as if you have trodden upon sharp knives. If you can bear this, I can help you.'

'Yes!' said the Little Mermaid, 'please give me the potion.'

'But you must pay me for my costly potion,' said the witch. 'You have the finest voice of all the mermaids; and it is with your voice that you intend to enchant your fair Prince. But this voice you must give to me as payment for my potion.'

'But if you take away my voice,' said the Little Mermaid, 'what will remain?'

'Your beautiful form, your graceful walk and your speaking eyes,' said the witch, 'with those you can capture a man's heart.'

The Little Mermaid looked afraid as the witch asked her if she had lost her courage. 'No, I have not lost my courage,' replied the Little Mermaid.

'Very well then,' said the witch, 'put out your little tongue so that I may cut it off for my payment.' And indeed the Little Mermaid put out her tongue and the Sea Witch sheared it clean off so that now the Little Mermaid was mute. As if this were not enough, the Little Mermaid had to agree that if she failed to win the love of her Prince she would immediately give up her life, be thrown into the sea and be turned to foam.

When the Little Mermaid drank the potion it felt as if a sword were splitting her into two pieces and she fell into a deep sleep. But when she awoke she saw the Prince standing before her and noticed that her fishtail had gone and in its place were two legs crowned with sweet white feet. The Prince led the silent beauty to his castle where they danced, every step biting her feet with a searing pain and in time the Prince became very fond of this silent girl but never thought to make her his wife. For he was to marry the woman who had discovered him upon the shore.

When the marriage day arrived, the Little Mermaid knew that she would die that night, for she had failed to win the Prince's love. But, as she stood by the shore soothing her burning feet in the ocean, her five sisters appeared. 'We have hacked off our hair and given it to the Sea Witch in payment for your life to be spared,' spoke the oldest sister. 'Here is a knife sent by the witch. Tonight you must plunge the knife into the Prince's heart and as he falls to his death, the blood that falls on to your feet will cause your fishtail to grow again and you may return to the sea as a mermaid once more.'

But when the night came, the Little Mermaid could not do the deed and instead hurled the knife into the ocean. With this defiance she gave up her life and was thrown into the sea where she melted into foam.

There are women in every city of every country to this day who get to the verge of killing their husbands to save themselves from life-threatening abuse. Few women respond to this urge; instead they stay mute and sacrifice themselves to their ordeal. For such women, giving up their voice in the hope of peace, as the Little Mermaid gave her tongue to the Sea Witch in return for the promise of love, is not enough. They must give up their lives and suffer the torture of walking on sharp knives, following in the agonizing footsteps of the Little Mermaid.

The girl who is made to silently endure terrible pains in total mute-ness is a common motif in many fairytales and is portrayed particularly vividly in the stories 'The Twelve Brothers' and the 'Six Swans', recorded by the Grimm Brothers and 'The Wild Swans' recorded by Hans Christian Andersen. In these tales a girl is born and all of her brothers either die or are turned into birds. When the girl realizes that her birth has caused the horror of her brothers' fate she agrees to all kinds of ordeals in order to restore them to life and human shape. In all of these tales, in addition to completing tasks set by a sadist with special powers, the girl must remain mute, refrain from laughing, weeping, singing or speaking a single word until her tasks are com-plete. Eventually, she is saved by a Prince who marries her in spite of her silence; or perhaps because he prefers it. The fate of the women in these stories is the fate of many women whose labour is suffered in silent pain, just as the Little Mermaid suffered her unrequited love in silence.

One of the sad facts in the story of 'The Little Mermaid' is that the Prince does not see that it was the Little Mermaid who saved him from drowning. He believes that the woman who discovered him upon the shore was his saviour. The Little Mermaid, meanwhile, cannot tell him because she has no voice. He is blind, she is mute. So many relationships are founded upon this mutual unappreciation of the other. One person struggles to keep the other alive and well and yet never feels that such work and devotion is seen. And to make matters worse, it is so hard for us to speak up for ourselves, even with our nearest and dearest. In fact it is often harder to find our tongue with those close to us than it is with a stranger.

The Little Mermaid represents the sacrifice of the voice in return for what we need. It is a sacrifice which we have all made to some degree – or have been encouraged to make. Like the Little Mermaid we bite our tongue, pinch our lips and repress our instincts, allowing the world to pass us by ignorant of our protest or our outrage, our desire or our insight. In the end, the Little Mermaid sacrifices herself. She dies mute and unheard and the Prince will never know that it is to her he owes his life. How many of us could die without ever having the truth of our soul voiced and heard?

The fate of the Little Mermaid is a particularly feminine one. In many fairytales, female virtue is associated with verbal modesty and restraint and a fair Princess is always softly spoken when she is not silent. Masculine virtue, meanwhile, is associated with an outspoken tongue and the courage to speak up and speak out. To overcome this misogyny, women must refind their voice. And, to recover the soul from its repressions, men and women must not be allowed to suffer in silence but must call attention to themselves through the power of the voice. We must all rediscover the power of the Siren.

The song of the siren

Bluebeard, a character in a tale written by Perrault in 1697, is like the prototype for all the deranged serial-killers and women-haters of present-day cinematic imagination. He lives in a grand castle where he houses a succession of wives. To each wife he gives a key which opens a door to a room which he forbids her to open and forbids her to enter. She must hold the key but refrain from acting upon her curiosity. But each wife is unable to resist and enters the forbidden chamber where she discovers the dead bodies of the previous wives hanging by a noose on a rail. Each wife's punishment for disobeying the master and using the key to unlock the morbid entrance is to join the bodies of all her predecessors upon the rack of ropes. But, the last wife has a sister called Anne whose voice is as loud and as piercing as a siren and she manages to call for help from the cliff top as Bluebeard is about to murder his next bride. Recognizing the voice of their sister, Anne's brothers gallop to the rescue and put an end to Bluebeard's scheme.

Anne's voice is a siren. It warns of danger and it attracts the heroes to the scene of the crime. Without Anne's voice, her sister would have met the fate of all the previous brides at Bluebeard's wicked hands. In many ways, Anne is the opposite or mirror image of the Little Mermaid. For, while the mermaid has no tongue, no voice and no possibility of sounding her soul, Anne's voice rings out loud and clear and brings men to her attendance with immediacy and urgency. Anne's brothers do not only hear her voice, they believe it. There have been other women, meanwhile, who have had an acoustic voice capable of entering the ears of men, but who have not been believed. For example, in Greek mythology, Cassandra told of the dangers ahead and warned that the land was in danger of being destroyed, but nobody believed her – until it was too late. This myth reminds us of the plight of young children who have been sexually abused and who manage to gather the courage to give voice to their ordeal. But no one believes them and they meet the same fate as Cassandra.

In the story of Bluebeard, Anne represents all that a voice can be: loud, sonorous, communicative, forewarning and ultimately a salvation. That is to say that Anne's voice is a siren.

In 1819, a French man called Cagniard de la Tour invented an instrument which emitted extremely high sounds. He named this instrument a *siréne*. Fifty years later his invention was adapted to create foghorns for ships. Cagniard de la Tour bequeathed the word 'siren' to common usage and this word is still used to describe machines which give warning of the presence of danger.

In Greek mythology the Sirens were sea nymphs with wings and claws and the body of a bird whilst their faces were human and as beautiful as any woman. But the Sirens' most astounding feature was the exquisite beauty and tremendous power of their voices which would charm and allure any who heard them sing. They lived on the rocky shores of the ocean, but unlike the foghorn adapted from Cagniard de la Tour's siren which stood upon the cliffs and steered ships away from collision, the Sirens lured the sailors towards them until they were irresistibly impelled to throw themselves into the sea to their destruction.

When Odysseus consulted Circe for sound advice before setting sail on one of his many voyages, she told him that his seamen should stop up their ears with beeswax before sailing past the Sirens' island so that they would not be lured by the Sirens' sweet song. She also advised Odysseus to have his men bind him to the mast before sailing past the island and that they should not release him until well clear of the Sirens' seductive call.

As the crew sailed passed the island, Odysseus could hear the ravishing melodies of their song. The Sirens' serenade was prophetic and promised him knowledge of all things that would come to pass on earth if he ventured into their company. Tempted by the Sirens' promise of knowledge Odysseus struggled to tear himself free from the mast; but his crew were faithful to his previous instructions and bound him faster to the wood. As they sailed, the music grew fainter until they were once again in the silent swoon of the sea, whereupon Odysseus was released from his bondage and the entire crew unsealed their ears. The Sirens were so vexed at failing to lure Odysseus that they threw themselves into the ocean and their voices drowned for ever.

A Siren is a temptress, a seductress. But she tempts and seduces with the promise of knowledge and foresight; and her voice is the carrier and emissary of all that she knows. The Sirens are named according to their voices: Aglaophonos, which means Lovely Voice; Ligeia, which means Shrill; Molpe, which means Music; and Thelxepeia, which means Spellbinding Words. The Siren's voice is one that enchants and beckons and its hungry call lures her prey. Men are both enraptured and terrified of the Siren's voice because it sings of things beyond their understanding.

In early stories, the Sirens could supposedly fly and if passing sailors did not respond to their call they would attack the ships from the air. In later times, stories were told of how the Muses stole their wing tips and left them earthbound and seabound. As tales of the Sirens passed from lip to tongue through retelling across the centuries they lost their claws as well as their wings and began to live not on the rocky shores but deep at the bottom of the ocean. In time, the Sirens became mermaids with the upper body and radiant face of womanly beauty and a fish's tail. But the mermaids retained the magnificent voice bequeathed by the Sirens of old.

Originally, the Sirens had a knowledge that was irresistible and made audible through the sound of their voice. It is this wisdom that was curtailed by those who muted the Siren's call, took away her wings and made her a harmless mermaid. This is a fate which so many have met: men and women. There is a voice in our heads, in our hearts and in our souls which holds a wisdom which cannot be undone – yet we have lost our tongue and feel afraid of voicing what it is we know to be true.

Reclaiming the muse

In Greek mythology the Muses and the Sirens, who embodied the power of voice and song, were women. Yet, for so long and in so many quarters, the instinctive and impassioned power of the feminine voice has been debased and silenced by the overpowering echoes of the spoken word, articulated by men. Many have tried to mute the voice of the soul and quell the power of its vibrations; and women have been the primary victims. In ancient Greece, the emperor Pericles was so distressed and unnerved by the relentless and infinite voices of the women wailing and keening at the funerals of their loved ones that he banned singing at the graveside. In these feminine songs of vocal passion Pericles heard a power greater than his rule, a power greater than an army of warriors, a power which threatened him. Throughout the ages, many women's voices have been suppressed and thousands of women have been punished for revealing their wisdom in sound. The notion of the wickedness of a woman's voice is highlighted in the Old Testament where, in the garden of Eden, Eve sinned through her voice, firstly by talking with the serpent and then by tempting Adam to eat with her words. It is a prevalent misogyny that women talk too much and men have perpetuated the belief that loquacity and an out-spoken tongue are a woman's vices while silence and verbal restraint are her virtues. Women, like children, are best when seen but not heard. This misogyny, which prefers the feminine voice to be quiet, has excluded entire societies of women from partaking in many singing traditions. Orthodox Jews forbid women singing during Hasidic ceremonies in the synagogues. English women of the Middle Ages were tortured for singing simple folk songs for fear that they were casting spells. And in present-day rural Greece, women are allowed to take part only in lamenting and funeral songs while the songs of joyous celebrations are reserved exclusively for men – an ironic turn of events that would make Pericles turn in his grave.

Yet, in many cultures, women have always been and remain the principal keepers and singers of songs which preserve their social traditions. Women are the keepers of song in the Balkans; women are the exclusive singers and preservers of traditional wedding songs amongst the Moroccan Jews in Canada; they are the exclusive transmitters of the rich array of lullabies amongst the Hazaras in Afghanistan; they are the leading vocalists accompanying Gamalan music in Java; and they are traditionally the keepers of songs which relay wisdom and foreboding, parable and myth to young children before sleep across Europe and North America.

To release the soul from enslavement we must reclaim the Muse; and the time-honoured way of achieving this is through the prophetic power of the singing voice. This power, though feminine in nature, is also accessible for men; but it means locating a respect for the magical intuition of fantasy; it means honouring the acoustic voice as much as the written word; it means accessing the anima from which song springs. Originally, fairytales were told by women and were often made up on the spot. Then, as men monopolized the domain of the written word and controlled the printing press, tales became masculinized, standardized and formalized. Reclaiming the Muse means

Voice Movement Therapy Exercise

The Soul Ballad

This is an exercise to be pursued for an hour each day spread over ten days; so firstly allot one hour a day which can be sacred for this work.

During the hour allotted on your first three days, sit quietly and write the story of your life. This autobiography should begin with your earliest memories and end with the present day. Write continuously and freely, committing to paper exactly what you recollect. At the end of the hour on your third day, read your autobiography aloud to yourself.

During the hour allotted on your second three days, rewrite your autobiography in the form of a fairytale. Use your autobiography to refer to and remind you of specific events. The fairytale should re-sculpture the realistic characters and actual events of your life story into amplified archetypal figures and fantastical scenarios. At the end of the hour on your third day, read your fairytale aloud to yourself.

During the hour allotted on the next three days, take both your autobiography and your fairytale and allow them to provide the inspiration for a set of song lyrics. This is called your Soul Ballad. Do not be concerned with melody but concentrate on the authenticity of your poetry. At the end of the hour on your third day, read your lyrics aloud to yourself.

Finally, on the tenth day, read your Soul Ballad three or four times, each time further amplifying the prosody of your speech into melody. Finally, sing your Soul Ballad with the complete canvas of your voice.

opening the mouth and letting melody and rhythm pour forth in-
tuitively through improvisation. Reclaiming the Muse means letting
go of fixed ideas regarding what is tuneful and what is not, what is
beautiful and what is ugly – for in the realm of fairytale the beast can
become a prince in an instant. Everything has two sides.

Reclaiming the Muse is the key to giving voice and giving voice
means having the right to speak up and speak out, to cry out against
injustice, to rejoice in triumph, to take a stand against oppression and
to make a noise in the face of complacency. Having a voice means
being able to state your opinion in public without being passed over or
ignored. Having a voice means being able to use the voice efficiently
so that people hear and feel the full weight of what you say. Working
directly on the voice encourages people to stand by what they truly
believe, to commit themselves to their convictions and to use a fully
expressive voice to state them. And one of the most inspiring ways to
reclaim this voice is to see your own life as a story, a tale and as a song
– and to sing this song aloud.

PART FIVE

The Healing Voice

CHAPTER FOURTEEN

Thou Shalt Not Cry Out Loud

*How singers were once healers and how history
ruined spontaneous song with rules*

The songs of ancient Greece

The people of many early civilizations revered the singer not as an entertainer, but as a healer who guarded the powerful wisdom of sound, which could alleviate psychic as well as physical problems. In addition, travelling singers throughout Europe preserved the ancient legends of old through their renditions of stories in the form of songs, raising the spirits of the listeners and stirring the sediment of their unconscious. However, as the church authorities began to control spontaneous singing with musical rules which dictated what could and could not be sung, the act of singing became increasingly a specialized activity serving to worship a God who it was imagined wanted to hear only sounds of purity. In addition, healing became increasingly the job of priests and medics. Consequently, the singer as healer became marginalized and forgotten. In recent years, however, many people have been awakened to the use of singing as a healing art and now wish to uncover their singing voice and use it in the way it was originally intended.

Despite the current return of the voice to the populace, the singer is still nowhere more revered than in the élite domain of the opera, where the beauty of the human voice occupies a cardinal place and where it attracts a showering of accolades. But taken from its pedestal and disrobed of the regalia of astounding sets and costumes, thundering overtures and scholarly interpretations, an opera is an old story, a myth, a fable or a legend told to music. And opera was first performed not in the great architectural palaces of London, Sydney, New York and Rome, but on street corners in ancient Greece. Here, lone players wandered the countryside with a small stringed instrument called a lyre, stopping wherever there was an audience and recounting the tales of the great myths. They sang the story of Oedipus, who unwittingly killed his father and married his mother. They told of the arduous labours of Heracles, who slaughtered the raging Nemean

Lion and killed Hydra, the nine-headed monster of Argos. They sang of Medusa's ferocious stare which turned men into stone; and they sang of the great Battle of Troy.

These nomadic songsters had chameleon-like voices which were vast in range and infinite in flexibility as they gave each character in their tales a distinct vocal quality while retaining a neutral voice when acting as the narrator. The singer would strum the lyre and screech and squeal as Medusa froze a man in his tracks, rant and roar as Oedipus gouged out his own eyes, yell the great battle cry as Achilles stormed into Troy, hiss and spit as the poisonous Hydra killed with its venom and roar the lion's death cry as the great cat fell beneath Heracles' club. The singer's voice leapt and turned, twisted and writhed in sounds of beauty and ugliness.

These solo renditions eventually turned into small ensemble performances which were the earliest form of Western theatre. Playwrights wrote the mythical stories as a dialogue and small groups of lone players came together and acted two or three characters each. In the transition from solo recital to ensemble productions, a new ingredient was added: the mask. Now the performers could identify each character by portraying each one with a dedicated mask as well as giving each one a specific vocal quality. The etymology of the English word 'personality' is inextricably linked to the use of the human voice to portray a dramatic character. The word 'personality' comes from the Latin *per sona*, which means 'the sound passes through' and was first used to describe the mouthpiece of the mask worn by actors. It then came to denote the character or person which the actor portrayed; eventually it came to mean any person and finally it took on the meaning that it now has for us. The word 'audience' also has an acoustic implication, for it comes from *audio* and means 'those who hear'. The etymology of these terms reminds us that the voice is integral to the way we communicate the nature of our character to those who hear us.

Greek theatre was a religious occasion. The characters which the actors played were gods, goddesses, heroes and heroines; in many ways the actors were invoking the appearance of the deities and they walked through the corridor between the divine and the terrestrial. These new masked theatre productions became one of the most significant contributions that the Greeks made to Europe's future cultural and artistic development. They precipitated the genesis of Greek tragedy: the great writings of Aeschylus, Sophocles and Euripides, whose plays were attended by thousands upon thousands of citizens.

And it was these performances that inspired the philosopher Aristotle to formulate his theory of catharsis.

Aristotle proposed the theory that the audiences who bear witness to these tragic dramas experience the fate of the central character as though it were their own. In particular, he hypothesized that the onlookers feel immense pity for the character's predicament and extreme fear in imagining that such a fate may befall them. According to Aristotle, investing belief in the theatrical portrayal in this way gave the audience a chance to purge themselves of the emotional energy generated by pity and fear and experience a genuine psychological relief which he called 'catharsis'. It was from Aristotle's description of the theatre that Freud and others took the notion of a cathartic therapy. Indeed, in ancient Greece, the art of theatre was related to the art of therapy and there was far less separation between the performing arts and the curative sciences than there is today. In Greek mythology, song, music and medicine were brothers and sisters. Orpheus, who was the keeper of song, Aesculapius, who was the mythical inventor of medicine, and the Muses, who were the mythical patrons of music, were all fathered by Apollo.

The great Greek mathematician and philosopher Pythagoras believed that music was at the heart of all things. Pythagoras recognized that sound is produced by vibration. He also recognized that all things from the great planets in the solar system to the tiny grains of sand upon the Aegean coast vibrate. Therefore, Pythagoras concluded that everything emits a sound, even though the ear may not be sensitive to the tone of all things. Furthermore, to the ancient Greeks, the fundamental principles of music – rhythm, melody and proportions of high and low, soft and loud – all these had their equivalent in the human soul. The right music could therefore bring an agitated soul into order and integration while the wrong music could throw the whole person into confusion, madness and disarray. Later, in Roman times, Cicero proclaimed that every emotion had a corresponding vocal sound and he compared the tones of the human voice to the strings of a lyre, both of which he believed could be tuned to represent perfectly all the changes in human mood and temperament. Later still, during the Renaissance, the notion of a vocal soul was further developed into principles for the composition of vocal music. Renaissance composers borrowed from the Greek philosopher Hippocrates the four elements of earth, water, air and fire as well as the four bodily humours of blood, phlegm, yellow bile and black bile and equated them with the four vocal qualities of bass, tenor, alto and soprano. Vocal music was then composed so as to create a proportional balance of the four vocal ranges and so induce an equilibrium in the humours of the body which in turn was believed to balance the soul.

Because ancient Greek theatre performances evolved from the solo renditions of singers, the use of the human voice remained central to the actors' tools; and as the individual actors invoked the gods and mythical characters with mask and voice, they were supported by a vocal chorus who sang, called and chanted in an exuberant mixture of prayer and narration, serving to work the actors and the audience into a climactic state. The actors and chorus did not recite their text in a fashion akin to daily speech, but with special sung intonations accompanied by the music of a lyre and a flute-like instrument called an *aulos*. To the modern ear this aspect of Greek theatre would probably sound chaotic and lacking in all melody. There was no concept of musical harmony and the combination of voice, pipes and strings did not serve to give a recital of a musical composition but to enhance the dramatic text with an exhilarating emotive sonority which led the audience to the pinnacle of their catharsis. It was not possible for the ancient Greeks to create musical harmony in the way that later European opera did because they did not have a system of dictating or writing music; they simply used the letters of their own alphabet to indicate notes on their scale, with some letters turned around to denote changes in the tonal colour of the sound. When the Romans infiltrated and overpowered Greek culture, they simply exchanged these letters for their own alphabet and continued the tradition of mounting dramatic productions which told of raging gods and supreme heroes, portrayed by actors and chorus whose voices came flooding through their masks.

The solemn church

It was the pre-Christian Romans who invented the organ and experimented with combining its airy sound with the sound of the singing voice. But as the institutional control of Christianity took hold, the great masked vocal theatre inherited from ancient Greece, with its wild quality of cathartic abandonment, wilted. Admiration, worship and celebration of the new deity now took on a more solemn form. An important part of the solemnity that is associated with early Christian worship is the way in which holy Scripture was uttered in such sorrowful non-elaborate tones by Church leaders and worshippers alike. This was a far cry from the spectacular vocal renditions that the

Greeks gave to their religious stories and which inspired the theatre of ancient Greek and Roman culture.

Although the Christian Church did not wish to inherit the masked revelries from its pre-Christian antecedents, it did develop the organ; and this instrument was central to the foundation of the very first singing schools in Europe which evolved during the fourth century. The aim of these singing schools was to train and ordain an élite breed of singers who could perform the musical services of the Church according to its taste by giving voice to the words of God in harmony with the authoritative solemnity of the organ. In an attempt to suppress the 'devilment' of any uncontrollable spontaneity, the Laodicean Church Council in 350 AD issued strict rules which limited the participation of the congregation in the sung services. However, because there was still no form of musical notation and no established musical rules, the singers and the organists often colluded in creating exciting and vigorous improvisations which upset the Church authorities who believed such displays of artistry to be incompatible with the reverence due to God. Consequently, the Church leaders made even more precise rules dictating the kinds of vocal sounds and combinations thereof which could and could not be used. The most famous of such stringent and punctilious rulings is that of Pope Gregory the Great (540–604), whose strict stipulations led to the creation of the Gregorian chant.

Over the next five hundred years, the language of musical notation slowly evolved, encouraging singers to limit their art to vocalizing the strange signs upon the page. But musical notation evolved slowly and failed so miserably to curb the vocalists' spontaneity that even as late as the eleventh century, a learned Benedictine monk called Guido of Arezzo said that in the church services it sounds not as if people are praising God but rather as if they are engaged in a quarrel. Guido set out to rectify this by making sophisticated changes to the crude system of musical notation which taught singers to remember the still unforgettable tonic scale: doh-ray-me-fah-soh-la-te-doh.

The formal structuring of music, which was developed primarily at the behest of the Church, completely altered the way singers used their voices. In Greek tragedy, although the vocal utterances of performers were organized by rhythm, pronunciation and prosody, such formal ingredients were born out of the desire to enhance the emotional canvas of the tale. In this new Christian service, however, the voice now served to articulate the written score which was attached to the words arbitrarily and in a manner completely dislocated from the emotive impulse generated by the utterance of the word. The passion of the mythical voice was lost and Christ's plea for a loud resounding voice of praise had been muffled by the stifling bishops' cloth.

Bards and bel canto

While the voices inside the Church became diluted and ameliorated by the strictures of the clergy, the streets of the world outside were still trodden by singers who were masters and mistresses of their own creativity. During the Dark Ages, which followed the collapse of the Roman Empire in Western Europe during the sixth century, lone players continued to roam the lands singing and telling their own stories with the aid of music. These singing tale tellers, who owed their birth to the ancient Greeks and who remained untouched by the demands of the Church, became a significant part of European song culture. In English, these men and women were called bards and fulfilled a spiritual function in keeping alive folk legends, myths and tales. But the bard is a worldwide figure who appears under a different name in various places: in France they were the troubadours, in Africa they were griots, in Norse they were skalds, in Anglo-Saxon they were gleemen, in Russian they were the kaleki, in India they were the magahda and in Japanese they were the zenza. These singing poets were sorcerers, stemming from a shamanic tradition. They did not sing only as entertainment but conjured illusion, invoked mortal and divine characters and ignited catharsis in those who listened.

In Italy towards the end of the sixteenth century, a group of learned artists formed an exclusive musical society with the aim of reinventing the magnanimous, spontaneous and inventive form of vocal expression used in Greek tragedy. Among the members of this society – known as the *Camerata* – was the great vocal soloist Giulio Caccini. He believed the Greeks had possessed a natural ability to express the full gamut of human emotions through the voice and sought to rediscover this ability in the voices of his students and to combine it with the skill of articulating sophisticated musical notation. It was from Caccini's vision that the school of composers and singers known as Bel Canto arose.

Bel Canto is an Italian term which literally means 'beautiful song' but which denotes the singing style which began in Italy and flourished throughout the seventeenth and eighteenth centuries as it was passed on through the classical singing schools of Florence, Rome, Naples, Bologna and Milan. The special art of the Bel Canto singers consisted of their ability to communicate a genuine expression of human emotion in all its nuances by taking their voice through all the

Voice Movement Therapy Exercise

The Vocal Orchestra

To begin, remind yourself of the three primary Harmonic Timbres of Flute, Clarinet and Saxophone. When you vocalize in Flute Timbre, imagine that the voice tube runs from the lips down to the indent between the clavicles at the top of the breastbone. When you sing in Clarinet Timbre, imagine that the voice tube extends from the lips down to the bottom of the breastbone. When you vocalize in Saxophone Timbre, imagine that the voice tube extends from the lips all the way down to the belly. Imagine that you are an orchestra made up of these three instruments and allow yourself to create an improvisational fiesta, jumping back and forth between the three instruments. As you limber up, begin to create the sensation and sound of other tubular instruments such as trumpet, trombone and bassoon, imagining that the tube changes shape and dimensions to suit the instrument at hand. As you explore your vocal orchestra, use the other ingredients of the voice to bring further colour and specificity to the instrumental sounds which you make.

colours of the sound prism, moulding their vocal instrument in infinite degree. Central to the technique used by the Bel Canto singers was the image of their voice as an elastic tube which could be moulded into a variety of shapes, forming different instruments.

The decline of multiplicity

The Bel Canto singers took their voices to new expressive horizons by concentrating on the long tube which ran from their lips to their throat without concern for fine anatomical details. But in 1741 the French anatomist Antoine Ferrain discovered two folds of tissue in the larynx whilst dissecting corpses which he called the vocal cords. Ferrain proposed that the sound of the human voice was caused by the vibration of these cords; and in the light of his propositions, singers and singing teachers began to concern themselves with a highly self-conscious attention to the throat as the producer of sound. With the tiniest understanding of anatomical knowledge, singing teachers began to fill in the blanks by concocting ridiculous explanations for the functioning of the voice.

Manuel Vicente del Popolo Garcia was a great singer and singing teacher who trained his son in the Bel Canto style but treated him harshly, beating him and degrading him in public regularly. While his sisters became famous for their singing, Manuel Garcia junior was a failure. Seeking to find the answers to his own lack of success, he took up the vocal cord theory of Ferrain. Inspired by the sight of a dentist using a mirror, he constructed a contraption with which he could observe his own vocal cords and became famous for inventing the laryngoscope – a small metal instrument which is placed in the mouth and which enables the larynx to be observed. When his father died in 1832, Manuel Garcia junior assumed the role of directing his father's singing school and without justification he acquired a reputation for being a great singing teacher. In his teaching and his writings, Garcia altered the Bel Canto techniques and developed an approach to training which he claimed was based on the true physiology of the voice.

The decline of Bel Canto singing may be attributed in part to the work of Garcia and his followers who abandoned intuitive and emotional insight in favour of insubstantial quasi-scientific analysis. But the dextrous and multiphonic voices of the Bel Canto singers were also made redundant by composers who wrote music for specific voices which remained within one range and quality. This encouraged singers to develop voices which specialized in a particular range and tonal colour and out of which the classical operatic voice specializations of soprano, mezzo, contralto, tenor, baritone and bass arose.

To reclaim the original power of the human voice that the Bel Canto singers possessed means we have to adopt their view of the voice as being like an array of instruments. Rather than concerning ourselves with the fine movements of the vocal cords and the intricate neuromuscular transitions which affect the larynx, we do better to concern ourselves with the voice tube and allow our imagination to conduct its flexibility of timbre. Yet, at the same time, we have to respect the physiology of the vocal instrument. I have had many people arrive in my consulting room whose voices have been wrecked by teachers whose methods have been blind to the subtle hormonal, muscular and neurological workings of the voice. But I have also had many clients whose voices have suffered at the hands of teachers who insist on a mechanical and physiological approach without compassion or regard for the heart and soul. To work in a holistic way with the voice means to appreciate both the psychic and the somatic dimensions of the voice; and this requires a careful and dedicated commitment to the art of imagination and the science of the body.

Ultimately, the vocalist has the answer themselves and the best gift which the healer can offer is a playful environment in which the client can discover their own method of vocal liberation. The act of play synthesizes art and science, music and medicine.

We speak of playing an instrument yet we rarely make time to play with our voice. When we are children, we indulge in vocal play to give voice to our inanimate dolls, to put sound to our model aeroplanes and to personify different characters. As we grow up, we lose this spontaneity and limit our voice to the sounds required. Discovering the healing voice means reanimating this capacity to play. Play is a universal human attribute. Just as no one has discovered a society without song, so there has never been a society which does not have play. Children learn who they are through play and adults lose the verve of their childlike spirit if they do not play in one way or another.

Music is founded upon play – though many musicians are so consumed with the rules of the game which dictate how to play their instrument that they often lose the capacity to play with it. The voice is no exception. The voice cannot be liberated through a rule-ridden regime of success and failure and the voice cannot be conducted by a brain that is obsessed with the finer details of the vocal cords. The vocal cords make the sound, but just as you cannot hear the sound of a tuning fork unless you place it upon a resonating body, so the tone produced by the vocal cords is only audible when resonated by the human body. Playing with the voice means playing with the body and allowing the body to act as the tubular body within which the bells of the human spirit are rung.

CHAPTER FIFTEEN

Groans and Moans and Tender Tunes

*How vocal sound can soothe physical pain and why
singing can help to make us well*

The ailing and the wailing

Sickness and song are sisters in the family of soul. Where there is music there is pain and where there is song there is an ailing. The great composers knew this as they scored their great works in the blood of their suffering. Handel was plagued with paralyzing rheumatism and developed cataracts which rendered him blind. Mozart, who died at thirty-six years of age, was continually ill from infancy when he suffered from fevers, skin rashes and recurrent streptococcal tonsillitis, then later contracted smallpox as an adult. Beethoven, aside from his deafness, suffered from chest infection, asthma and bowel disease which tyrannized him with painful diarrhoea and frequently left him exhausted and dehydrated; he died of cirrhosis of the liver. Paganini, who had all of his lower teeth removed by an incompetent dentist and lived on a diet of liquid and medication, spent the last years of his life in agony with laryngeal disease and severe abdominal pain, eventually dying of the symptoms initiated by syphilis. Rossini suffered from chronic gonorrhoea, as well as respiratory and cardiovascular diseases. Schubert suffered from syphilis and typhoid fever. The entire Mendelssohn family died of strokes. Chopin suffered from a debilitating lung disease which killed him at the age of forty-nine. Liszt suffered from chronic bronchitis, arthritis, poor vision and heart disease. Grieg had respiratory illness and terrible rheumatism. Bizet died at thirty-six after a lifetime of ill-health, including chronic streptococcal throat infections and rheumatic fever. Brahms died of cancer of the liver. Britten died of a stroke. Debussy died of rectal carcinoma; and Shostakovich died of motor neuron disease.

But it is not only in the great classical epitaphs that we can hear the body singing its ailments. All singing genres echo their fair share of faltering health. A nursery rhyme as simple as 'Ring a Ring of Roses' is based on the bubonic plague; the jazz and blues song tradition is predicated upon tales of depression and anguish; many musical theatre productions contain songs about death and dying; a vast number of British and North American folk ballads tell the tale of a sick and poorly fellow or maiden; and opera is rife with madness, pathology and ultimately death. There are also many singers of the contemporary age for whom music has been or is the balm, the medicine and the saviour that has helped them deal with their journey through difficult times. For music, especially vocal music, helps us sing through the darkness. Singing provides perhaps not a cure for pain but a cure from the further agony of having no means to express that pain.

It is the most natural thing in the world to express our feelings when we are sick through groans and moans which serve to comfort and alleviate pain. By developing these sounds we can use the voice to heal both ourselves and others of sickness. The live singing voice has been successful in helping people awake from comas; has helped people remain calm during surgical operations when a general anaesthetic has been prohibitive; and it has been used to help sick children get

Voice Movement Therapy Exercise

The Vocal Balm

Like the exercise called The Holding Voice described in Chapter Two, this exercise is ideal for two people.

In this exercise the person who is to offer their healing heart gets into a comfortable position where they feel secure, balanced and able to provide compassion and sensitivity. The partner with a physical hurt that requires healing allows themselves to curl up in their tactile embrace, snugly easing into their arms, pressing themselves into their lap and allowing themselves to be rocked and cuddled, soothed and solaced by their physical containment. The hurt person then places their hands on the part of the body that is pained and begins to vocalize in moans and groans. The person offering healing then also places their hands there and joins the vocalization. Both partners should imagine that their voice is a liquid balm penetrating the surface of the pained part of the body and easing underlying hurt.

The person who is hurt then allows words to be articulated and the person offering healing repeats the words until a duet is born. Both partners then sing the healing song.

better for centuries. As Pythagoras realized, vocal sound is fundamentally vibration and throughout history the vibratory nature of
sound has been used to impact the cells of the body causing them to
reconstellate in a healthy way.

Feeling hurt

There are few people who would not admit, at least to themselves,
that they carry with them the burden of some kind of hurt – either
physical or psychological. Indeed, the main reason why people seek
healing of one kind or another is because they reach a realization that
they can no longer carry the burden of pain, discomfort or unease in
their mind, body, heart and soul.

The hurt of the psyche can take many forms: the hurt of depression,
the hurt of sorrow, the hurt of loneliness, the hurt of panic, the hurt of
fear and the hurt of anxiety. All these manifestations of hurt take their
toll on a person's psychological constitution and if they continue
unabated they can create the sensation that the person lives in a
traumatized state. Very often, psychological hurt results in the first
place from a specific trauma such as the trauma of bereavement, the
trauma of sexual abuse or the trauma of a terrifying accident. In
other circumstances, psychological hurt may have accumulated
in response to an ongoing traumatic situation, such as the trauma of
an emotionally oppressive relationship.

Eventually, psychic hurt becomes somatic pain as the residue of our
trauma becomes localized in a particular part of the body, where it is
likely to manifest itself as a physical illness or dysfunction. Intermittent
headaches, skin rashes, disturbances of sight and hearing, stomach
ulcers, digestive problems, frequent diarrhoea, aches in the skeletal
muscles and major dysfunctions of the primary organs such as the
liver and kidneys have all been related to a psychogenic origin. In
cases where a part of the body somatizes psychic pain, it is as though
the body acts as a physical memory of a psychological trauma – what
we may call a 'body memory'. The body is capable of remembering
psychological trauma in the form of somatic pain, discomfort, disease
or dysfunction even when the conscious mental memory appears to
have forgotten the event or events which caused the trauma. And
much of this emotional residue is somatized in our organs.

The organics of emotion

Our organs organize our emotions. Without our organs our emotions
would run like flooding waters and burn like an uncontained fire.

Organs are vessels in which we may keep our feelings freshly stored and preserved; and the two organs which form a supreme partnership, reigning over our organic emotional life, are the heart and the stomach.

The human heart is languid and moist and pulls blood through the body just as the moon pulls on the tide. The beat of the human heart keeps time like the rhythm of a song and the percussion of its motion is scored into our veins like music scored upon the page. When we sing it is because our heart rises like a wave and carries our voice upon its crest. The heart is an orchestral quartet of chambers: two chambers for oxygenated blood and two chambers for blood that is spent and awaiting the fresh vitality of the air which we breathe. In days of old, before the surgeon's knife discovered the biology of things, people believed that the heart was a single vessel full of blood and feeling. The heart was the seat of all things felt and those who acted on their feelings were considered brave and lion-hearted. Now we know better. Now we know that the heart is divided against itself and at all costs must keep oxygenated and unoxygenated blood separate. To let them mix would bring on a chemical disaster. Our emotions are also often divided against themselves. We often seek to keep two feelings separated from each other for fear of exploding. Yet keeping the alchemical fluids of our psyche apart for fear of trouble uses a huge amount of energy and can exhaust the soul.

The heart is a superficial organ; it is close to the surface of the body and when you place your hand upon the chest you can feel it beating. The emotions associated with the heart are also those which are close to the surface of our soul; they are the feelings which pervade our life in constancy. We speak of wearing our heart on our sleeve and our heart is exposed and vulnerable to the blows and torments, the elations and joys of humanity. Looming like the beacon upon the shores of these sentiments is love; and our heart is the hot-bed of our loving self. When Eros shoots his arrows he aims for our heart; when we fall in love it is our heart that races; and when love leaves us it is our heart that feels broken. Our heart has its own memory, and the walls of its chambers are adorned with the faces of all our Valentines. Love keeps the heart soft and those soft-hearted among us who love too much can crack the heart in many places, leaving it porous like sponge adrift in the Pacific. Yet there are those too who are hard of heart, for whom love has long since departed or perhaps for whom love never entered in. The loveless heart is like a rock, stoic in the face of adversity and relentless in its isolated independence. For to love is to need; and to sing from the heart is to open up the channels of our desire and plead for the food of our soul.

Many people come to discover the healing power of their voice and bring with them a hardened heart. They can sing from high to low and from loud to quiet; they can combine Free Air with Violin; they can move from Modal to Falsetto Register and pass from Flute through Clarinet to Saxophone Timbre. Yet when all is said and done they look up with an expression of empty dissatisfaction and despair at the absence of felt emotion. It is as though the heart has been separated from the voice. Sometimes, to leap over the barricade which is drawn across the path between heart and throat, it is necessary to give up an attachment to the familiar voice. This may mean deliberately defacing and subverting the sweet gleaming surface of acoustic beauty and digging up the dark dank soil beneath the polished notes. For all that is in the heart is not pure and if the voice were always pure it would be transparent.

The stomach does not beat like the heart. The stomach is not divided into chambers like the heart. The stomach is a single vessel which churns and smoulders, ferments and stews. The stomach is a holding place, a vessel of alchemical storage where the acid and the alkaline of our instincts brew. Everything that we have swallowed and stomached is clustered here. Everything we have wanted to say but have kept from our lips is in the stomach. Every instinct we have wanted to gratify but have tamed and tempered is ablaze in the stomach. Every unfair blow, every terrifying shock, every unmourned loss, every ungrasped love is adrift in the tidal sea of the stomach. Because the stomach effervesces with such chemical intensity, it is the place where many fresh feelings are concocted. The stomach is a place where plots are hatched, where schemes are construed and where we may find the motivation and the seething determination to rise up out of the subservience of our swallowing into the power of our ultimate regeneration. When we feel motivation and inspiration in the stomach, we know it is for real and we know it is time for change. When we feel the voice rising from the stomach, we know that we are sounding out our deepest and oldest self and tapping a source of feeling deeper than the sentiments of the heart.

While the heart houses the ostensible sentiments that we can wear upon our sleeve, the stomach is often the location for the less pervasive and infrequent of life's feelings, such as grief. When in love we place our hand upon our heart; but in grief we place our palms upon our belly. The stomach is close to the guts and when faced with loss, grief can leave us feeling gutted. Like Orpheus, many people sing out of loss. Singing fills the emptiness in our stomach, it satiates our hunger for the milk of human kindness, it calls forth the angels to watch over us and releases our demons into the air.

When we sing from the belly, from the guts, from the womb, we re-establish our emotional territory. When we sing from the depths it can feel as though our bones quake. It is as though singing from the lower regions vibrates to our very foundations so that we might build our-selves up again from the roots. Going down into the depths with the

Voice Movement Therapy Exercise

The Voice of Heart and Belly

Create a Spherical Space and map out the four points of a compass, limbering your body and exploring your Breathing Pattern. Get into a position where you feel close to your emotions and place your hand on your chest in the region of the heart. Begin to vocalize in Clarinet Timbre. Imagine that the voice tube begins at the lips and travels down into the centre of the heart. Sing as though the voice comes from your heart rather than your larynx and allow the sound to be filled with your heartfelt emotions: consider where your heart has been broken, where your heart is soft and where it is hard, where you have the courage to love again and where you are empty of hope. Combine the ingredients of the voice until you find a combination which expresses your feelings most poignantly. Allow yourself to cry as you sing and imagine that the contents of your heart pours up through the voice tube in sound.

Now place your hand on your belly and allow the voice tube to expand and the sound to change to Saxophone Timbre. Imagine that the voice tube begins at the lips and travels down into the centre of the stomach. Sing as though the voice comes from your belly rather than your larynx. Continue to vocalize, recombining the ingredients of the voice to find a sound that expresses the feelings in your stomach. Consider what you have had to swallow and stomach; where you are aggrieved; what you have lost; and what fresh life you are pregnant with. Allow yourself to cry as you sing and imagine that the contents of your belly pours up through the voice tube in sound.

voice is like the descent into the Underworld that Orpheus undertook. It enables us to reclaim the lost parts of ourselves, the passions and appetites which life has caused us to put on hold. But it is a descent which also releases the three-headed hounds of our animality. We may discover voices which sound monstrous and atrocious, as though the contents of our guts were being miraculously distilled into sound and regurgitated through our mouth.

The voice is an arena in which we can allow potent emotions to combine, producing explosive results which have an artistic and creative effect rather than posing a threat of destruction. During my years of work as a voice therapist, I have heard people release sounds so volcanic and volatile that you could feel the earth shake. Often, beneath these sounds is a conduit of anger, rage and retaliation as the vocalist gives voice in a moment to all the injustice that they have had to bear over years. When the voice releases itself from bondage, it is as though all the bittersweet emotions which have been stored in the heart and stomach over decades come rising up in sounds of mythical proportion.

Catharsis and recovery

One of the oldest and most well-established models of mind–body functioning is the cathartic paradigm. According to a cathartic view, the human organism is a hydraulic system capable of receiving and dispensing energy. Energy enters and leaves the psychic and somatic system in a variety of ways. Energy can enter the body through the ears, so that when someone shouts at us, verbally abuses us or whispers sweet words of love to us, the energy in our system is increased. The same amount of energy may then be dispensed from our system if we verbally retaliate, physically punch our verbal aggressor or return the loving compliment with a kiss. Energy can also enter the system through the eyes. If we are exposed to a terrifying sight or if we set our eyes upon something of incredible beauty, then our psychic energy is increased. And this energy can be released through our behavioural reactions, such as running away, screaming or singing the praises of the beauty that we behold.

The cathartic model proposes that to maintain health, the system must be kept in a state of energetic balance. Moreover, to keep the system in a state of balance, the same amount of energy which enters the system must in turn be released. However, there are many factors which prevent this from occurring: fear, intimidation, shock and a host of social prohibitions often prevent people from responding equally to the energetic events which influence them. As a result, a build-up of psychic energy occurs, causing an increase in pressure within the system.

Many people experience psychological pain because they have been traumatized either by a single event or by an ongoing situation; and the consequent pain is often the result of an accumulation of emotional energy which has not been discharged. A cathartic therapy is one which provides someone with an opportunity to discharge this accumulated energy in a safe place, as though reliving the original trauma but where the person is enabled to react to it and to retaliate. In order for a genuine catharsis to be facilitated, there has to be an open channel through which psychic energy can be released – and the voice provides such a channel. When someone is offered an opportunity for a vocal catharsis, it is as though the emotional flood-gates come bursting open and a historic backlog of unexpressed pain comes flowing out, leaving the person with a sense of having been relieved, perhaps even purged.

CHAPTER SIXTEEN

The Sounds of the Psyche

*How voice can ease a troubled mind and why
singing often works better than talking*

Going up, going down

The fortunes of life go up and down and our feelings rise and fall with
them. In the turn of the moon our joys may turn to sorrows and our
merriment may slip into misery as the zenith of our ascent slides
towards the void of our decline. We cannot guarantee the permanence
of our emotions; they rotate like a carousel; they dip and dive like a
roller coaster; and they draw us into the vortex of their irresistible
magnetic pull. And each person must face their own unique emotional
reflection. However, there are certain universal feelings which befall
us all and unite humankind in the commonality of emotional experience. At the centre of these universal feelings is an emotional quartet of
two conditions and two passions which are deeply influential in their
effect upon our voice. The two conditions which most determine the
tonal colours, the overtones and the undertones of our voice are
depression and mania. The two passions which most determine the
hue and flavour of our voice are grief and rage.

To claim the abundance of a liberated voice means allowing the
sound of our soul to be filled with the sediment of this quartet. If we
cannot give voice to depression, mania, grief and rage, then we are
sentencing the greater part of our emotional self to silence; and this can
only lead to despair. Many people who seek a healing journey through
their voice are not suffering from the touch of these emotions; rather
they are suffering from the silencing and quashing of them. For as soon
as our feelings have a voice they no longer seek revenge for having been
ostracized by eating away at our unseen and unheard heart.

The depressive in the cellar

As we swim in the ocean of our emotions we try desperately to escape
the immobilizing catacombs of depression. For some, depression
signifies a passing period of lethargy and disengagement; for others it
spells a loss of enthusiasm and a sense of pointlessness; but for many,

depression is a monopolizing force which blows through the soul like a gale, bringing with it the despair of an abandoned soldier in the trenches of an endless war in an unnamed country at an unnamed time. For those whose psychic skin is sensitive to its touch, depression is an abuser *par excellence* which tears down the walls of hope and determination and leaves the debris of emptiness in its wake. Depression can paralyze the muscles of body and soul; it can strike a brazen man dumb and leave a rowdy woman speechless. Depression does not amplify the voice, it stifles it. Thus, a voice which has been sequestered by depression and which has become overly drenched with its dew can soak the listener with its damp, dank vapour.

In the midst of depression's ensnaring claustrophobia we can use the voice to loosen its grip and rise above its downward pull. Depression loathes the energy of sound, particularly high sounds. Depression prefers silence in which it can fertilize its soil; if pushed it can also tolerate the inert hum of low sounds which warm its morbid bones. But depression is evicted and uprooted by sounds of ascending levity and exhilaration.

To move ourselves out of depression we therefore need to vocalize on an ascending scale. But depression is no fool and will not be bullied, jolted or kicked from its seat. First we must befriend its sullen tones and harmonize with its tune, taking it gently by the hand and inviting it into our arms. For behind the overpowering dogmatism of depression that drowns out our exuberant spirit with its interminable drone is a sad and lonely figure desperate for a tender embrace. When I work with people who find themselves in the grasp of depression, I always advise them to gently slip around behind it, take it in their arms and hold depression in a sonorous embrace.

When you feel depression infuse your soul, vocalize low tones so that the vibration warms the loins and take depression on a slow waltz around a deserted ballroom, finding a groaning moaning melody which remains in the dark blue hue of a melancholic refrain. Then as depression is rescued from its despairing loneliness and begins to let down its guard, allow the voice to ascend towards the heights where the fresh sun breaks. The ascent must be even and slow because depression has a sharp nose and if it smells a trick afoot it will waltz straight back to the damp cellars of the soul. As the voice ascends the scale, find crescendos where light seeps into the voice and causes a peak of volume and a surge of enthusiasm. But do not try to pretend that depression has been beat. Let the mournful blue of the deep tones underpin the higher notes like the depth of painfully earned wisdom which sits beneath a seemingly trivial insight. For we need depression.

Depression, though often our enemy, is the silt in the river of our affections and can be mined, polished and preserved like a jewel. For a voice without the sediment of depression is a voice which lacks the smell of the soil. Pretty voices which smile and perform virtuous tricks may be musical to the last, but in their perfection they serve only to disappear into their pristine irrelevance. Voices which crack and smoulder with the blemishes of life may not meet the standards of the classical musical convention, but they will always be the voices which stir the passions and ignite the furnace in the belly. And many of these voices come from the mouths of those who have danced the tango with depression. To the singer, depression is an art, a pursuit and a mode of experience. When depression rears its head it is because the waters have run clear for too long and the river must be made murky lest we forget the rich life that lives beneath the current.

Depression confronts us with the psychology of gravity. Like gravity, depression pulls us down, keeps us rooted and tempers our heady aspirations with the humility of our bond with the ground. A voice without depression is a voice without gravity and a voice without gravity has no roots but floats and escalates into thin air.

The maniac in the attic

While depression languishes and smoulders in the cellar, the maniac meanwhile tears through the attic like a lunatic possessed. Mania is the tornado which terrorizes our relaxation with the daunting recognition that there is work to be done, energy to be spent and things to be sorted. Just as depression is buried too deep beneath the floorboards to hear the frantic racket of mania, so mania is too high in the eaves to notice the morose moaning of depression down below.

Depression begs for tenderness, for contact and for a slow waltz, but mania performs the jitterbug with a fleeting narcissistic display. For mania is too busy, too preoccupied and too engrossed to care for a dancing partner. Mania moves alone. Mania is oblivious to the presence of another and too intent on grasping the future to notice the flavour of the present. Mania gobbles, devours and regurgitates the atmosphere, breathing quickly in order to extract enough oxygen from the cool air of the altitudes. Mania knows no gravity and will not be held down by the principles of the earth. Mania lives in suspension.

For some, mania is a passing phase of industrious activity; for others mania is the chemical child of adrenalin which plays havoc in the playground of the soul; for some mania is the excitement which provides drive and ambition; but for many, mania is a white hot flame which burns the soles of the feet and sends the body and soul into a delirious spin. Those who are prey to the appetites of mania reside in the dominion of anxiety. For anxiety is the blood in mania's veins; anxiety is the food in mania's belly; anxiety is the wind which keeps mania airborne. Anxiety is mania's life force.

Mania keeps the psyche on the move; it can desecrate the home of peace and make an entire family of psychic forces homeless. Mania can make a pilgrim into a fanatic and turn quiet contemplation into plaguing rumination. Mania does not amplify the voice; it deforms and distorts it. While depression's aria is a droning hum, mania's retort is a hiss and a buzz. Mania cannot hold a tune but spits out a medley of clamour. Mania is the god of noise. Thus a voice which has been sequestered by mania's urgency and which has become electrified by its voltage can agitate and derange a listener with its current.

In the midst of mania's mesmerizing discontent we can use the voice to dull its blare and clear a settled dwelling along its thorny trail. Mania detests the energy of low sounds and slow songs. Mania prefers the dazzling heights of the upper octaves and the raving crescendos of up-tempo show-stopping tunes which pander to its agitation. But mania is humbled and conquered by sounds of descending introversion which embarrasses its lack of fastened stability. To move ourselves out of mania we need therefore to vocalize on a descending scale. But mania is as smart as the estranged sibling in the cellar and will not be anaesthetized, subdued or tranquillized by threat or intimidation; and if deep tones are introduced without wit and panache, mania will drag them up to the attic and turn their balm to acid in an instant. For mania to settle it must exhaust itself; so first we must befriend its screeching yells and harmonize with its tune, taking it firmly around its spinning waist and matching its tirade with equal fervour. For behind the frenetic fever of mania with its seething white noise is a somnolent and slumberous figure desperate for abeyance and reprieve. When I work with people who find themselves in the grasp of mania, I always advise them to slip into its orbit and collaborate with its whirl and listen to its needs.

When touched by mania, vocalize fast, loud, high refrains and take mania on a vigorous jitterbug or polka or jive around the dance floor, finding a sizzling and impulsive melody which remains in the bright white light of an eruptive and sparkling refrain. Then as mania staggers to keep afoot and begins to reveal signs of fatigue, allow the voice to descend towards the soporific roots where the dusk sets in. The descent must be even and slow because mania has bright eyes and if it sees a flaw in your slight of hand it will jive straight back to the insulated attic of the soul. As the voice descends the scale, find elongated and protracted notes of meditation and sustain where darkness covers the voice with an eiderdown of warm seclusion. But do not try to pretend that mania has been beaten. Let the ardent and excitable frivolity of mania's high tones linger above the dark river of the depths like the early mist above an age-old lake. For we need mania.

Mania, though often our enemy, is the flurry, the zest and the zeal in the marrow of our bones and can pervade our lives with savour and delight as we imbibe the fluids of its inspiration. For a voice without the elevations of mania is a voice which lacks the giddy abandon of flight. Strong centred voices which seduce and appeal through technical virtuosity may be musical to the last, but in their perfection they serve only to disappear into a superfluous dispensability. Voices which crackle and sputter with the disarray of life may not kowtow to the fastidious ears of the classical musical convention but they will always be the voices which resound in the chambers of the heart. And many of these voices come from the mouths of those who have burned both ends of the candle with mania. To the singer, mania is a trade, a vocation and a calling. When mania rears its head it is because the silt in our waters is beginning to drag us down into the seriousness of life's concerns and a fresh spring of carbonated hope must burst through lest we forget the rich life that hovers in the seemingly empty heavens.

Mania confronts us with the psychology of flight. Mania whips us up, keeps us in the air and tempers our terrestrial self-importance with the humility of our heavenly destiny. A voice without mania is a voice without flight and a voice without flight has no lift and so cannot lift the spirits of those to whom it sings.

When we unchain the voice from the mediocrity of its narrow range it runs like a freed prisoner towards the extremes. The liberated voice touches the heights and the depths. But this inevitably animates the emotions stored at the extreme ends of the scale. This means that we must be ready to waltz with depression and quickstep with mania as we listen for the fresh voice of vitality that emerges when these two disunited siblings of the psychic family sing.

When grief remains

Grief carves a cavern in our belly where the song of our sorrows seems to echo for ever. Grief seems to have no end and a beginning which cannot be forgotten. Grief digs a hole in the pit of our stomach, and the earth which piles up from where the hollow has been quarried coagulates in the throat where it chokes us with every word we speak. Grief surrounds the voice with its shroud of frailty. Grief is the lump in the throat that is as dry as our tears are wet.

Beneath our muffled croaks we know that if we were to sing it would be a farewell lament. But the pain of saying goodbye in the dawn of grief is a terrible ache. And when all is said and done there lingers only the futility of what remains. No sweet caress, no promising opportunity, no sunset or sunrise and no pleasure untold will rescue us from the torrential sorrow of death's conviction. Behind our sweet sunken eyes, our spirit swoons as our hope fails.

In the melancholy of our loss we ourselves become lost as we search in vain in a sea of familiar but uncomforting glances for the face of our dear departed, like a tiny child separated from a mother in a crowd of well-meaning attendants. But they are gone and we have to refind ourselves without the embrace of those who once were with us.

There is no heartfelt voice which does not bemoan the sting of grief. An authentic voice is always laced with the sorrow of mourning. Happy voices that are jovial and bright may entertain and charm, but if they are not underscored with the loom of mourning they will not stir the passions of the heart.

Orpheus sang out his sorrows when he lost his beloved and when we sing, like the infant child, we call out to have our losses recovered and our loneliness relieved. For we are hungry for love and singing stays the silence of our destitution. In singing, a lone soul may live as though another were present. Our voice is our lost love and when we sing with amorous regard, we wake our dormant love from the slumber of reminiscence and kiss once more the cheeks of those who linger just a breath away. But grief does not need a funeral to descend. We can be aggrieved by all that we have lost and by the loss of that which we never truly possessed.

The raging fire

When our anger simmers it circles inside us, souring our juices, flushing our skin and knocking at the inside of our chest like a drunken vagrant. But when our anger peaks it becomes our rage and pours outwards. When we exhale the winds of our hidden fury, our rage soon becomes our outrage; and when rage is out, tempers will fly. Anger is a brooding introvert which mulls and muses, brews and fumes. If anger stays inside it can eat a hole in the stomach with the acid of its pungent resentment as it chews over its bitter options. But if anger becomes rage, takes leave of its enclosure and sounds its fanfare to the world it can demolish the esteem of those who stand in its passage. There are many who keep anger under lock and key for fear that they might annihilate the opposition and have to face the irreversible destitution of their regret and grief. Yet we often raise the roar of our anger because we are in mourning.

Anger and grief are sisters in the family of psychic forces and when we feel angry it is often because we have been aggrieved. Anger rears its head when something has been taken from us and we are plummeted into the loss which remains in its shadow. It is awakened by the grief which descends when our self-confidence is taken by someone who undermines or belittles us. Anger is mobilized by the grief

Voice Movement Therapy Exercise

The Quartet of Passions

Create a private Spherical Space and begin to move around it as you breathe in and out through your mouth. As you dance, locate the four points of the compass within your sphere: north, south, east and west. Begin vocalizing, combining the palette of vocal ingredients freely and spontaneously.

Now begin to find four different combinations of voice and movement which express the quartet of elements: depression, mania, grief and rage. Then locate each of these four elements at a specific compass point.

Move through your Spherical Space, vocalizing from your soul, moving in and out of the four compass points as you move in and out of the four elements; as though when you physically leave the north of your sphere and journey towards the south, you also leave the element that you have located at the north point behind you and move into the element which you have placed at the south of your Spherical Space.

When you are steeped in the passion of one particular compass point, abandon yourself fully to the felt sensation. But when you depart; let the element go with equal dedication. As you become more accustomed to the radical changes you will begin to experience a catharsis. This is the vocal dance of the two passions and two conditions.

which falls when our trust is stolen by someone who deceives us and is vitalized by the grief which transpires when someone special is prematurely taken from us. Anger is animated by the grief which ensues when we witness the suffering of the innocent. Anger is the commotion mustered as the psyche tears itself away from the catatonic shock of grief's wounded soul. Grief is the hollow lament which echoes in the ravine beneath anger's tumbling landslide. The question for us all is whether we can turn our introverted anger into extroverted rage so that we may avoid becoming the victim of our own fury without destroying those whom we wish merely to address.

From hurt to healing

To be effective, a healing process cannot end in a catharsis and the silence which follows the echo of vocalized pain. One of the problems with a cathartic experience is that the relief can turn out to be short-lived and the trauma can quickly reconstellate as vigorously as before. This can lead to a cyclical dependency on some kind of cathartic release where we are never really free from a repetitious return to an original hurt. In my experience, in order for the cathartic relief to be long-lasting, it is necessary to take hold of the discharged emotions and make artistic use of them by forming sound into song in the true shamanic tradition.

In the course of an evening concert, a singer may sing a variety of emotionally charged songs from up-tempo light-hearted love songs to sorrowful ballads of desperation. In one song the singer may be beaming with a smile and genuinely feel full of glee as she sings; in the very next song the singer may weep and be genuinely full of sadness. If the singer is also the writer of her own songs, there may be a time, during the original writing of the song, when the singer is overwhelmed with emotion, particularly if she is drawing the song from her own traumatic experience. In many ways, the writing of the song may provide for a certain catharsis. The healing occurs in the next phase where the song can be sung with enough recollected authenticity of the original trauma to ensure an emotive realism but with enough distance to ensure that the rendition of the song is artful. This is what I call 'artistic distance'.

One of the most important things that this artistic distance provides is the ability to reap pleasure from pain. For the singer will experience the act of singing as highly pleasurable while at the same time experiencing some of the pain that the song may describe. Indeed, many singers will testify that the more painful the subject of the song the more pleasure is reaped from singing it. It is as though singing enables us to link arms with pain and remember its inevitable place in our life without finding our self immovably clasped by its grip.

To find the healing power of voice is to find the singer within. At first, a flood of sound is poured out, giving acoustic shape to deep emotion, very often of an extremely painful kind. But in time, this outpouring is familiar enough to be heard as the rudiments of a song and can be formed. At this point, we can be freed from a cycle of cathartic discharge.

Blood and sorrow

Janice was a professional musician. Her primary instrument was the French horn. One night at the height of her career, on her way home after a concert, Janice was consecutively raped by three men. Two of the three men took turns to hold her to the ground whilst the other raped her. Despite the severe physical pain and the extreme emotional shock, Janice could barely make a sound throughout her ordeal. She tried to scream but could only produce a muffled shout which was soon silenced when her oppressors covered her mouth with their hands. Since the ordeal Janice had been consistently breathless and felt a constant physical constriction around her throat. Her voice felt paralyzed. She came to work with me to try to regain some vocal strength and overcome the breathlessness but she also hoped to heal some of her deep emotional wounds.

When Janice vocalized it was very quiet, high in Pitch, in Flute Timbre and Falsetto Register with a fair amount of Free Air and quite a lot of Violin. The sound also had a gentle Pitch Fluctuation which created the quality associated with someone who is nervous, perhaps even afraid. Janice said that when she vocalized, especially on a long continuous note, she felt the 'iron bar' tingling all the way down her chest.

Janice moved and vocalized in her Spherical Space over a period of about fifteen minutes as her expressions went from fear to indignation to triumph. At times her voice sobbed and her body shook; at times she yelled in despair; at other times she called out: 'Get away, get away.' As she called out these words, Janice held on to my arm with a vice-like grip, pulling me towards her. I whispered to her, 'It's all right, I am right here.' At this point, she put her other hand on her chest and said that it was 'warm and tingling'.

I asked her to lean over from the waist and imagine that the voice was pouring out of her like a liquid; and she began vocalizing in a series of long sounds like the siren on a ship. I asked her to imagine that she was singing down into a well and that her voice echoed in the open abyss. Her voice now opened into Saxophone Timbre. She was very hot and clammy and her breathing Frequency was very quick with the most exaggerated movement focused in the area of Thoracic Expansion.

Janice now came up to standing. Her face was red, her pupils were dilated and her hands and arms started thrashing about. As her arms gyrated, her voice whizzed round and round in siren-like sweeps. Her voice had changed radically and was now deep in Pitch, extremely loud, in Modal Register, Saxophone Timbre and all the Free Air had disappeared. She started ascending the Pitch range in Saxophone Timbre going all the way up to a piercing whistle in Falsetto Register, which she sustained for about a minute before breathing and repeating it again. The piercing whistle-like scream went on and on as though it would never stop. As she vocalized, I asked her to imagine that she was a great white bird, flying above the cool Pacific, swooping and gliding; and I asked her to improvise a melody in this ultra-high range. She began to sing in a voice so clear and so high it would have made the audience at Covent Garden fall from their seats. Her arm movements became wing movements and her voice whistled on.

Eventually, Janice came to stillness and I asked her to continue vocalizing and go down through primate, into feline-canine, over on to her side and then on to her back. She later told me that she was terrified that if she got on to her back on the floor her voice would disappear again and she would not be able to move. She was afraid of finding herself back in the paralyzed silence of the rape again.

Janice vocalized and went down through the cycle. As she rolled over on to her back, her legs went up in the air, her arms gyrated and tore the air to shreds as her voice reached its crescendo. Then she leapt up on to her feet, sung out and fell back down to the floor again, rolling over on to her back. She went round and round this cycle, proving to herself that she could vocalize fully and move freely from the position in which she had been raped to a triumphant standing position.

When she stopped, I asked Janice to write a set of lyrics that expressed her experience which she then read aloud.

> The iron in my chest
> The rage in my heart
> The blood in my womb

> The poison in their eyes
> The sorrow in my soul
> The danger in my trust
> The ending of this tale
> Has now become a must
> Listen to my voice
> And let me live again

We now returned to vocalizing in the high whistle in Saxophone Timbre which she had discovered, but this time she sang the words – like a diva. Over the next few weeks, Janice wrote a number of songs and sang them, both in her sessions with me and on her own. Her breathlessness decreased and her voice returned; and she soon returned to playing in the orchestra.

Taking possession

When Janice's work with me came to an end she said that though the intensity of her catharsis in the sessions had been a core part of her healing, it was the channelling of the discharged emotions into her own songs which gave her the self-empowerment to move on. When we write and sing our own songs, the material of our pain takes artistic shape and becomes something more than the residue of our suffering; it becomes sacred, communicative and elevated.

To discover the healing voice it is necessary to allow the most raw and unformed sounds to emerge from the conflictual battlefield in our heart. But the healing begins when the battle ends and the harmony of peace is celebrated in a song.

CHAPTER SEVENTEEN

Falling Apart and Composing Our Selves

*How each of us is made up of many personalities
and why each one should be given a voice*

The mask and the mirror

The material of the voice is sensual and sensory. We hear it through the senses. Frequently we hear the voice as though through the sense of touch. We feel pinched, slapped, compressed, pierced, hammered, stroked, tickled, or shaken by a voice. We hear the voice as though through the sense of taste, listening to the despondent bitterness, the citrus tang of jealousy or the sugary sycophantic sweetness. We hear the colour of a voice, the deep blue of melancholia, the green of envy and the red of retaliation. We may also feel the temperature of a voice, which can be experienced as warm, cool, burning hot or ice cold.

It is not just the listener's senses which are affected by the voice. Often, the presence of a particular vocal quality also affects the way the vocalist perceives herself. Our own voice feeds back messages to us through our own ears. Our voice reaffirms who we are, how we are feeling and what we are seeking. The voice serves an important function in maintaining our sense of identity, for the sound of our voice reminds us of who we are; it reinforces our sense of self. In the same way that our identity is continually reaffirmed by the visual reflection provided by a mirror, so too the sound of our voice enables us to hear reflected an audible expression of our own image. Consequently, changing the voice has the potential to alter both the way others perceive us and the way we perceive ourselves.

As time passes we often become over-identified with a single image of ourselves. We become dominated by the image of our self as a particular character. We may become stuck in a childlike image, in a dominating and bombastic image, in a kindly and self-effacing image. And all of these self-images find expression through the quality of vocal tones.

Because the echo of the tone of our voice in our own ears is so important in reaffirming our own image, we become caught in a vicious circle. The bitterness or anxiety which we hear in our voice serves only to reinforce the image of ourselves as bitter or anxious. The childlike-ness or aggressiveness which we hear in our voice reinforces the idea of our self as a child or an aggressor. If our psyche becomes so saturated with a single emotional tone, it may become difficult for us to communicate anything else and, without warning, the voice simply lets us down. We may wish to express a particular emotion or image, such as anger or authority; or we may need to instil confidence or calm. But our voice has become so identified with a particular aspect of ourselves that it cannot move. It is as though the voice has become a rigid mask which we are unable to take off. A person with such a mask may feel mature but sound childlike, may feel enraged but sound intimidated, may feel saddened but sound unmoved; they seek help but their voice signals self-certainty; they seek warmth and affection, but their voice signals guarded detachment; they seek respect but their voice attracts belittlement. Often this can cause the person some distress, for what people hear on the outside bears no relation to what the person feels on the inside.

A multitude of moods

Expanding the range of the voice and allowing it to dance freely through all of its colours provides us with an opportunity to step outside our familiar mask and reanimate the entire kaleidoscope of our per-sonality. Psychologically, this enables us to visit and express those parts of the self which have hitherto remained in the dark and undercover.

To do this it is necessary to peel back the layer of spoken words which keeps deep emotion under wraps. We must once again allow the voice to holler and roar, screech and lament. By transforming the voice in this way, we can effect changes in the sense of self. We can provide an opportunity for every individual to hear themselves afresh. Then, when someone can hear themselves as something more than the familiar limited personality that they have become accustomed to, this new refreshed person can be voiced outwardly for others to hear.

When we peel back the mask we often discover more than we had expected. All the world is a stage and upon it we play many characters; for each one of us is made up of many selves which transpire and evaporate as each moment solicits the company of our many guises. We play our roles according to the scene, reforming and adorning our psyche with the discreet mannerisms of each distinct part that is especially crafted for the audience at hand. We are each a luminary of ephemeral and impermanent alteration before God as we pass through the seasonal masquerade of our multiplicity. We play pioneer in the field and coward at sea. We act as parent in one house and slip seamlessly into the temperament of a child in another. When we are intimidated by authority we may bend low in our obsequious and ingratiating servility; and when we are afforded the privileges of leadership we may with equal comfort indulge our contemptuous and supercilious condescension. Some scenes draw out our charitable pilgrimage whilst others provoke our sanctimonious disdain. In the company of our brother we are meek and acquiescent yet in the company of our sister we become bold and audacious. Towards our own needs we may be harsh and insensitive, yet when we hear the needs of another we may become resourceful and philanthropic. On a night blessed with warmth and good company we may be the outrageous jester; yet on a winter's eve in the company of sorrow we may be the morose and sullen stooge.

The nature of our personality is conjured at the whim of our moods. Moods are the magician of the soul, transforming us from one shape and colour to another, ensuring that we do not settle in the deadly complacency of our monocentric and habitual addiction to safe but uninspiring familiarity.

Moods come and moods go; they are like spirits suspended in the atmosphere where they satellite the psyche passing in and out of our orbit and directing the energetic forces of our character. Moods cannot be placated or appeased, they will not be fettered or manipulated. Moods must have their day and they appear in an ever-unsuspected sequence, dancing their delirium upon us, their hosts.

A mood is a condition of mind, a sentiment and a predicament. A mood brings with it a persona, a behaviour and a character. A mood is like a musical motif or key which runs through the composition of our self for a given time before transposing to a fresh refrain. Moods make different personalities of us. Our moods swing like a psychic pendulum forever reminding us that we are blessed with a fair serving of choice regarding who we are and who we become. Moods are our dancing partners and though they will not be made puppets to our autocracy they will be charmed, persuaded and flattered; they will be our comrades, our compatriots and our confidants. But if moods are ignored or belittled, denied or disavowed they will soon make themselves our demons and contenders, pitting themselves against our will, subverting our intentions and sabotaging our desires. Moods will not be cut out of the picture; they are not an editorial choice. For without moods we would be subject to the tyranny of our single-minded appetites. We would become one and one only, without malleability or manoeuvre, without a margin for error and without the essential transformations of character that make each hour, each day and each lifetime rich with diversity and multitude.

The multitude of sub-personalities which constitute our self have their carnival and fiesta when we dream. In the dark hours the nocturnal canvas of our sleep is animated with bizarre characters, beguiling creatures, portentous situations and ominous journeys. Each element of the dream is a part of our self: whether animal, vegetable or mineral, our multiplicity is reflected in each symbolic object, each perfunctory occurrence, each prophetic vision. When we dream of a child, we encounter the child in us. When we dream of a turbulent river which flows in both directions, we meet the part of us which agitates in indecision. When we dream of broken glass, we confront that part of us which has been shattered. When we dream of old friends, we rediscover our own lost youth. There is not a single corner of the dreamscape that is not cluttered with a part of us transformed into the optical language of our night-time reveries.

Each sub-personality that constitutes our self and is made optical through dreaming also has a voice. When someone begins to discover the flexibility of their voice, a thousand characters and images come flooding forth in sound. Singing is dreaming awake. Singing is the acoustic and sonorous expression of our many selves. In discovering the complete range of the human voice we become truly multiphonic. For we have not one true voice but ten, twenty, a hundred, a thousand. Finding your true voice is a misnomer and a misdirection. Finding your true voices in their multitude is where the healing lies.

When times get rough we are often told to 'pull ourselves together' as though falling apart into many pieces were undesirable. But in fact, we are really composed of many different personalities, each with their own moods, feelings and instincts and perhaps we need to allow ourselves to fall apart with a little more ease and a little less anxiety. Each of the inner characters which form our grand self has a voice which often chatters away in our heads, each one laying out the reasons for and against a particular direction we may be thinking of taking. One voice may be that of a cautious and considerate play-it-safe character, another may be that of the risk-taker, another may be that of the loving parent, whilst there may also be a voice of rage and loathing. By using the voice to give acoustic expression to each of the sub-personalities which make up our whole being, we can release the chatter from our heads and allow the various selves to create a symphony of co-operation.

The circus of the soul

Mary came to experience a healing journey through her voice because she felt 'stuck'. She had no major symptoms and no specific life issues for which she sought a resolution. She said simply that she wanted to 'break out of her shell'.

Mary's voice was genial and tender with a wispy emission of Free Air. The higher the Pitch the more gentle, soft and unassertive it became, revealing a girlish frivolity and fragile delicacy. Whenever I asked Mary to make a sound I noticed that she would gently sway from side to side; so I asked Mary to exaggerate the swaying as though she were on a swing and to increase the childlike quality of the voice as I led her up the scale into a higher octave.

As the notes began to get higher and more difficult to sing, Mary contorted her face and clenched her fists, which brought to the sound a degree of fracas and commotion, as though the child within her was having a tantrum. I asked her to sing as though the baby were spoilt, irritable, incensed and protesting, and as a result her voice became more animated and multiphonic. She opened and closed her fists as she stamped on the ground and her voice increased considerably in volume, whistling through the studio like a siren.

I then asked Mary to move to a position on all fours and dance her shoulders in an undulating ripple of waves. I suggested that she howled as though from the belly and the sound now assumed a canine quality like that of a baying wolf. I asked her to imagine that her hackles were up and that she was howling a warning and protective shield of sound around her cubs, which lay curled beneath her belly. The Pitch descended and the sound became guttural and marauding, echoing as though in a cave. In the deeper pitches the sound was wolf-like; in the higher pitches it was feline; in the middle there was an ambiguous animalistic quality, half wolf, half cat, like a beast from a beguiling world of creatures concocted from an amalgam of animal instincts.

I now asked Mary to develop the opening and closing of her fists as though she were a creature extending and retracting her claws in preparation for a fight. At the same time I suggested that she decrease the volume of the sound and sing with an alluring, tantalizing and ravenous tone, part lion, part Siamese kitten, part wolf. As she sang, I continued to suggest tonal images: feline, predatory, devouring, spiteful, provocative, protective. Mary became a creature with young offspring, prowling around her young, spitting with venom, with foreboding and intimidation, developing a voice made of acid which was caustic, ungracious and scathing.

Bringing Mary back up to standing, I suggested the image of a gigantic Parisian chain-smoking animal lover with six children who wore pearls and bellowed and bawled. Mary's voice became darkly enfolding as I suggested a collage of images: mouth full of caviar, a voice like molasses or like tar, an attitude of belligerent certainty. Her voice became that of a prolific and world-famous Parisienne lion tamer and a new character emerged as the studio thundered with the voice of 'Madam Felineou'.

Mary now began strutting around the studio singing improvised arias on the words 'I am Madam Felineou', like a prima donna. She mimed smoking with a cigarette holder. Her whole face altered radically from the attitude it expressed at the beginning of the session and any visible or vocal signs of innocence and vulnerability had long since receded. The voice and physicality of this shy gentle woman was now dominant, proud and unnerving.

As I watched the backwards and forwards motion of the cigarette I asked Mary to magnify and inflate it, so that it became the whip that spurs horses. Mary now began driving a chariot and her voice took on a hot-blooded, ambitious and barbarous tone. I encouraged this transformation by suggesting tonal images: Boudicca, the wild woman of the forest, calling a revengeful war cry, leading the warriors into battle and rounding up a tribal mass of agitated protesters. Mary's voice and body was now involved in an opera of blood-curdling melody as though the studio were full with an army of female revolters.

By this time Mary was beginning to tire and so I slowed down the pace through gentle instruction. I suggested that the dead lay scattered and the wild woman now felt sorrow for the victims. The voice returned to a higher Pitch and she sang with compassion as though uttering a prayer for the dying or a contemplative chant on the futility of war. Mary stood swaying as she had done at the beginning of the session and I asked her to blend different aspects of the acoustic journey into a single voice. The irritable child, the vulnerable kitten, the howling wolf, the wild woman of the forest, Madam Felineou and the unbridled warrior became less separate and distinct voices and more aspects were audible in a single tone. The voice sounded to me as if it truly belonged to her. But it was multifaceted, embracing a spectrum of images any one or combination of which could emerge as the dominant factor at any time.

The multiphonic soul

For many people on a healing journey, the biggest threat to their soulful liberation is monophrenia. Unlike schizophrenia, which yields a splitting and fragmentation of psychic contents making identity impossible in the face of eternal inconsistency, monophrenia causes the opposite problem. Monophrenia ties us so immovably to a stable single-centred notion of ourselves that we become stifled by the lack of variety. Monophrenia arises from the trauma of enforced routine. So many of us are confined by the rigours of repetition, which makes everyone else feel safe in the knowledge that they know who we are. Our change makes them nervous because when we discover a new voice, their ears have to adjust to a new frequency. Yet we must not respond to the complacent demands of those who require us to sound familiar. We have too much of ourselves to resound.

Discovering the healing voice means, above all, discovering the variety of the soul and giving each molecule of its ether a unique sonorous frequency. There are not eight notes in an octave but thousands; and there are infinite combinations of vocal ingredients which give rise to millions of voices each of which is distinct from all others.

Our healing rests in our dedication to change. Our healing rests in our commitment to continually reconstellating our voice in a search for unsung harmonies. Our healing rests in the knowledge that the best constancy is the repetition of reinvention.

Your Voice and Your Future

*How to further unchain your voice, where to find
practical guidance and what you can do next*

Having read this book and explored the exercises in each chapter, you
may want to extend your healing journey and further liberate your
voice from inhibition. If you wish to experience Voice Movement
Therapy and the ideas presented in this book directly, there are a
number of opportunities available.

Correspondence Course

You can undertake a healing journey of self-discovery wherever
you are, through the Voice Movement Therapy Correspondence
Course. This is a learning programme combining personal growth,
self-investigation, practical exercises, creative projects and theoretical
study. The course guides you through a safari of self-discovery,
enabling you to liberate your voice, unleash your creativity and revive
your spirit.

The programme is designed to offer people from all walks of life an
opportunity to benefit from Voice Movement Therapy and at the
same time acquire a respectable qualification. It also offers people a
chance to study under the direction of Paul Newham wherever they
are located.

The Correspondence Course is accredited by the Oxford &
Cambridge University and Royal Society of Arts Examination Board
and awards certification in the Core Principles of Voice Movement
Therapy.

Details of the Correspondence Course can be found in the complete
prospectus and accessed via the Voice Movement Therapy website.

International Workshops and Training Programmes in Voice Movement Therapy

The London Voice Centre offers a full training in Voice Movement
Therapy as well as short introductory courses and workshops in all

aspects of the healing voice. All programmes are accredited by the Oxford & Cambridge University and Royal Society of Arts Examinations Board and are directed by Paul Newham.

Though the London Voice Centre is located in England, programmes are often held in the USA and other countries. Details and dates for all courses are given in a comprehensive Voice Movement Therapy prospectus and are also provided on the Internet at the Voice Movement Therapy website.

Individual Voice Movement Therapy Sessions

The International Association for Voice Movement Therapy is a world-wide network of trained practitioners who have attained the Oxford & Cambridge University and Royal Society of Arts Examinations Board professional Diploma in Voice Movement Therapy and who offer individual and group sessions in Voice Movement Therapy.

There are currently practitioners in the UK, Europe, North America and Canada. There is, however, a great need for more Voice Movement practitioners, as there are not enough to meet the demands of clients; and there are many areas without a resident practitioner.

A current list of practitioners and their location can be mailed to you by request or can be accessed on the Internet at the Voice Movement Therapy website.

Special Needs

If there is not a qualified Voice Movement Therapy practitioner near you, or if your needs cannot be met by Voice Movement Therapy, there may be another kind of practitioner or organisation in your vicinity who can help you. If you cannot locate a practitioner and have found it difficult to find alternative help, please contact The London Voice Centre with a brief description of your situation and Paul Newham and his colleagues will endeavour to point you in the right direction whenever possible. Information and assistance with finding help can also be found on the Internet at the Voice Movement Therapy website.

Books, Audio and Video

Paul Newham has produced a number of resources for those wanting to utilize Voice Movement Therapy techniques including:

- *The Singing Cure*, a complete audio course with vocal demonstrations, exercises and an accompanying study guide.

- *Shouting for Jericho*, a feature-length video which shows Voice Movement Therapy in action and includes special film revealing the inside of the voice box during vocalization.
- *Therapeutic Voicework*, a comprehensive encyclopaedic book on the history and theory of vocal healing.

Paul has also produced a collection of audio recordings and a series of text books on specific aspects of voice work. Details of all available resources are given in the Voice Movement Therapy prospectus and can be obtained by contacting the London Voice Centre or by accessing the Voice Movement Therapy website.

Voice Movement Therapy Website

The Voice Movement Therapy website is a multi media interactive resource providing:

- current news and information on Voice Movement Therapy
- a confidential discussion forum for members
- a shop of recordings and publications
- a current schedule of programmes
- a full prospectus which can be downloaded and printed

Prospectus & Further Information

A full Voice Movement Therapy prospectus, containing a current schedule of programmes, a catalogue of recordings and publications and an up-to-date list of qualified Voice Movement Therapists, can be mailed to you by request or can be accessed via the Voice Movement Therapy website. Requests for these materials and all other enquiries should be addressed to the London Voice Centre.

The postal address is:

Voice Movement Therapy
The London Voice Centre
PO Box 4218
London SE22 0JE
UK

Tel: (+44) (0) 181 693 9502
Fax: (+44) (0) 181 299 6127
Email: info@voicework.com
Website: www.voicework.com

Glossary

Abdominal Expansion: swelling of the belly that occurs on inspiration during optimal breathing.

Acoustic Soul: that part of our being which can only be expressed in sound.

Allopathic: allopathic medicine is the approach to illness which underpins traditional Western medicine and which tends to see the mind and the body as separate entities.

Amniotic Fluid: liquid in which the foetus is suspended in the womb.

Anima: refers to the feminine aspects of a male psyche.

Animus: refers to the male aspects of a female psyche.

Apollonian: from the name of the Greek god Apollo, meaning ordered, logical, formal, sober and rational.

Archetypal: archetypes are aspects of the human psyche which are universal and found in the dreams and fantasies of all people. Something is archetypal when it is a universal quality or aspect of the psyche.

Articulation: shaping of vocal sounds into distinct units by the mouth, tongue, lips and jaw to form the vocal components which combine to constitute words.

Attack: impact between the two vocal cords during vocalization. Attack may be soft or hard or anywhere on the spectrum between.

Bacchanalian: taken from the Greek women known as the Bacchae, who followed Bacchus (also known as Dionysus) on his journeys, bacchanalian means frenzied, ecstatic, wild, intoxicated and sensuous.

Breathing Pattern: overall manner with which someone breathes and is comprised of Physical Expansion, Pressure, Frequency, Volume, Depth, Tube Configuration.

Cacophony: a loud discordant noise.

Catharsis: purging, exorcism or release of intense negative emotions.

Chest Register: term used in classical music to describe the quality of voice which the singer has in the lower pitch range. Also known as Modal Register.

Clarinet Configuration: shape and size of the voice tube when the larynx is held in the middle of the neck and the diameter of the tube is neither fully contracted nor fully extended.

Clarinet Timbre: quality of voice produced when vocalizing with the voice tube in Clarinet Configuration.

Clavicular Expansion: elevation of the shoulders which can occur on inspiration during breathing.

Depth: how deep or shallow the inspired breath is drawn into the lungs.

Dionysian: from the name of the Greek god Dionysus, dionysian means intuitive, irrational, chaotic, exuberant, elated and wild.

Disruption: breaking up of a vocal sound by friction, silence, tension or anything else which interferes with the production of a smooth tone.

Diva: term given to a renowned female opera singer.

Elemental: something which is an absolutely fundamental ingredient.

Falsetto: quality of voice with which a male counter tenor or female soprano sings. It is also the quality which accompanies the higher notes in yodelling. In classical music this is often also referred to as Head Register in a female voice.

Flute Configuration: shape and size of the voice tube when the larynx is held high in the neck and the diameter of the tube is fully contracted to its narrowest dimensions.

Flute Timbre: quality of voice produced when vocalizing with the voice tube in Flute Configuration.

Free Air: unvocalized expired air which brings a breathy quality to the voice.

Frequency: how many times we breathe in and out, or inspire and expire, in a given unit of time. Frequency also refers to the amount of times per second that an object, such as the vocal cords, vibrate in a second and which determines the pitch,. The higher the frequency the higher the pitch.

Harmonic Timbre: quality of the voice that is determined by the configuration of the voice tube and which can be Flute, Clarinet or Saxophone.

Head Register: term used in classical music to describe the quality of voice which the singer has in the upper pitch range. Also known as Falsetto Register in a male voice.

Holistic: an approach to the human condition which perceives the mind and the body, the individual and the community, the environment and the inhabitants and all other aspects of life to be fundamentally connected in such a way as to influence each other.

Holler: a form of shouting which has been developed into singing styles, such as the American Blues Holler and many indigenous work-song styles, where the music is born from the necessity of communicating over long distances.

Improvise: to vocalize freely without following a set melody or lyrics and without using a written score.

Issues: term used in psychotherapy to denote the emotions, thoughts, memories, concerns, fantasies and ideas which a client has at any one time.

Laryngologist: a medical doctor specializing in disorders or diseases of the larynx.

Loudness: how loud or quiet the voice is, determined by the pressure of the breath released from the lungs.

Modal Register: quality of voice which a male opera singer uses and which a female classical singer blends in with her Head Register. It is also the quality which accompanies the lower notes in yodelling. In classical music this is often also referred to as Chest Register in a female voice.

Muezzin: vocalist who calls the faithful to prayer in Islamic religion.

Nasality: quality of voice produced when a lot of sound is directed through the nasal passages. In Voice Movement Therapy this vocal quality is called Violin.

Physical Expansion: stretching and enlarging of the torso during inspiration.

Pitch: how high or low the voice is, determined by the frequency with which the vocal cords vibrate in a second. Also referred to as 'note' or 'tone'.

Pressure: force with which air is drawn in during inspiration and expelled during expiration.

Primal: refers to the most basic aspects of the human psyche which are inborn, instinctive and primitive.

Primordial: refers to the earliest times, before civilization as we know it. Often, the term refers to an aspect of the human psyche which originates in the most primitive distant past.

Prosody: melodic rise and fall in pitch which underpins the speaking voice. Prosody is the music of talking.

Psyche: taken from the name of a Greek goddess, this term literally means 'soul'. In modern psychotherapy, psyche usually refers to a combination of mind, soul and imagination. It is the location of our thoughts, feelings, dreams, fantasies and aspirations.

Psychosomatic: whilst the term 'psyche' refers to the ephemeral world of feeling and thought, the term 'soma' refers to the palpable world of the body. The term psychosomatic therefore describes a psychological issue which is expressed through the body as a sensation or illness.

Register: when a series of notes is sung with the same consistent quality, this quality is called a register. There are two main registers known as Falsetto and Modal Register – also known as Head and Chest Register. There are also two other registers known as Whistle and Vocal Fry.

Repression: refers to the burying of experiences, often painful ones, to the point where we often forget that they ever happened. It is also possible to repress certain emotions or thoughts, especially if they are disturbing to us. Repression can be deliberate or can happen without us being consciously aware that we are doing it.

Resounded: term used when a sound reverberates and rings and seems to fill the space all around us.

Saxophone Configuration: shape and size of the voice tube when the larynx is held at the bottom of the neck and the diameter of the tube is expanded to its maximum dimensions.

Saxophone Timbre: quality of voice produced when vocalizing with the voice tube in Saxophone Configuration.

Shaman: a combination of priest, soothsayer, sorcerer, doctor, healer, poet and performer who in many indigenous non-Western cultures used voice and song to revive the sick.

Sonic Embodiment: to use the voice and body to give complete expression to an aspect of our self.

Sonorous: something which vibrates to produce sound.

Spherical Space: private invisible arena which surrounds each person and which we carry with us wherever we go.

Soma: the living body.

Somatic: something which expresses itself through the body.

Soul: for many the term 'soul' refers to the seat of our spiritual aspirations. In modern psychotherapy, however, 'soul' is often used interchangeably with 'psyche' and is thought to be the location for our thoughts, feelings, and imaginings.

Thoracic Expansion: elevation and protrusion of the upper chest that occurs on inspiration during optimal breathing.

Timbre: means 'acoustic colour' and refers to the quality of voice with which a note is sung. Timbre is therefore any vocal quality apart from the pitch.

Transpersonal: those aspects of a person's psyche which do not originate in their particular past or experience.

Trauma: an event or experience which causes a severe shock to the psyche or body with ongoing consequences.

Tremolo: a light flutter running through a series of notes used to decorate and embellish the singing in classical music.

Tube Configuration: shape and size of the voice or breathing tube during vocalization or respiration which can be Flute, Clarinet or Saxophone.

Violin: quality of voice produced when a lot of sound is directed through the nasal passages; often referred to as 'nasality'.

Visceral: deep instinctive sensations usually experienced bodily.

Volume: refers to the size of a space such as the amount of space created in the lungs during breathing. In Voice Movement Therapy 'volume' refers to the amount of air that is inspired and expired.

Index

Abdominal Expansion 78, 80, 81, 86–7
adult relationships 147–49
Aesculapius 163
American Indians 123
ancient Greece 34, 155, 161–4
anger 183–5
animal metaphors 114–15
animus and anima 76, 134–6
anxiety 181
Apollo 102, 120–1, 163
Aristotle 163
Armstrong, Louis 69
Arnold, Eddy 54
artistic distance 185
audience 103, 162
Australian Aborigines 123

babies
    and the mother's voice 16–19
    pre-verbal voice 12–13, 21
    sounds before birth 11–12
bards 166
Bee Gees 54
Beethoven 16, 170
Bel Canto 166–7
Bizet 170
Bluebeard 152–3
body 89–90
    'body memory' 172
    organs and emotions 172–6
Brahms 170
brain hemispheres 24–5
breathing 75–7
    Depth 85–6
    Frequency 82–3, 85, 86, 87
    Physical Expansion 77–81
    Pressure 81–2
    Tube Configuration 86–7
    Volume 83–4, 87, 86
Britten 170
Buddha 106
Buddhism 123–4

Caccini, Giulio 166
calling 6–10
Cassandra 153
castrati 134
catharsis 121, 122, 163, 176–7, 185
chakras 123
changing tune 30–1
Chapman, Tracy 54
chi 123
children
    early environment 93
    effects of musical training 26
    emphasis on logic 25
    language development 21–3
    mutism and phonophobia 142–6
    and play 169
Chopin 170
Christianity 124–5, 164–6
Cicero 163
Clarinet Configuration 57, 59, 64, 81, 86
Clarinet Timbre 57, 60–4, 81, 86
Clavicular Expansion 78, 80–1
cradling 17–20
Cronos 82
crying 99–100
    and release 109–10
Cyrano de Bergerac 133

David and Goliath 124
de la Tour, Cagniard 153
death 144–5
Debussy 170
depression 178–80
diaphragm 78
Dietrich, Marlene 65
Dionysus 120–1
disability (handicap) xii, 128–30
dreams 192
Dylan, Bob 65

Echo and Narcissus 148
emotion 89
    organics of 172–6

endocrine system 133–4
Eurydice 102–3
Eve 155

Falsetto Register 53–6, 136
Farinelli 134
feminine aspects 134–6, 152, 155–7
Ferrain, Antoine 167
Flute Configuration 57, 58, 80–1, 86, 87
Flute Timbre 57, 58–59, 80–1, 86
Ford, Tennessee Ernie 54
Freud, Sigmund 32, 33, 163

Garcia, Manuel 168
Garfunkel, Art 66
glossolalia (speaking in tongues) 124–5
glottis 44
Greece see ancient Greece
Gregorian chant 165
Gregory the Great, Pope 165
grief 182–3
Grieg 170
Guido of Arezzo 165

Hades 102
Handel 170
Hauser, Kaspar 111–12
heart 173–4
Hinduism 123
Hippocrates 163
Holiday, Billie 65
holistic healing xv–xvi, 72–4, 168
hormones 133–4

incongruence 23–4
instinct
    and order 120–1
    and voice 12, 112–14
intuition and logic 24–5
Islam 124

Jesus Christ xiv, 124
Joplin, Janis 69
Joshua 124
Judaism 124, 155

Laine, Cleo 60
language 4, 111–12
    development 13, 21–3
Laodicean Church Council 165
laryngoscope 168
larynx 44, 57, 69, 72, 91, 134
laughter 105–7
Leo XIII, Pope 134
Liszt 170
'Little Mermaid, The' 149–2
logic and intuition 24–5
London, Julie 66
love talk 133

mania 180–2
masculine aspects 134–6, 152
memory 32–38
Mendelssohn family 170
mental illness 143–4
Miriam 124
Mnemosyne 34
Modal Register 53–6
monophrenia 194–5
Monroe, Marilyn 28, 67
moods 191–2
Moses 124
mother-child relationship 16–20
movement 89–90
Mozart 170
Muses 34, 154, 163
music
    effects of formal structuring 165–6
    effects of formal training 25–6, 106, 169
    and memory 34
    and the soul 163–4
mutism 142–5

New Testament 124, 125

Odysseus 153–4
Old Testament 124, 155
opera 161–2
Orbison, Roy 54
Orpheus 102–3, 163, 176, 183

Paganini 170
Paul 124
Pericles 155
personality 162
pharynx 44
phonophobia 145
play 106, 169
prayer 125–30
Presley, Elvis 54
prosody 26
psychic hurt 73–4, 172
psychic menagerie 114–15
Pythagoras 163, 172

redemption 38–9
Rodgers, Jimmie 54
Rossini 170

Saxophone Configuration 57, 59, 60, 81, 86–7
Saxophone Timbre 57, 59–60, 81, 86
Schubert 170
self
    image 189–90
    mutiple aspects 190–2
    in space 90–3

sexual abuse 36, 153
sexuality 50, 55, 67, 133–6
shamanism 122–3
Shostakovitch 170
sickness 170–2
Simone, Nina 60
singing xi-xvi
    in ancient Greece 161–4
    bards and Bel Canto 166–7
    and crying 99–100
    and emotional expression 140–1
    and faith 124
    and healing 161, 171–2, 185–6, 188
    imposition of rules 164–6, 167–9
    infants' 17
    instinctive nature 27
    intuitive and logical aspects 24–5
    Memory Songs 34–8, 100–1
    and multiple selves 192
    primeval and universal xiv, 3–6
    redemption songs 38–9
    releasing the soul 156–7
    and sexuality 67, 133
    shamanistic 122–3
    songs of loss and longing 103–5
    women and 155
    see also Bel Canto
Sirens 153–4
'Six Swans, The' 151
soft palate 64
soma see body
Somerville, Jimmy 54
soul
    and breath 76
    loss and reclamation 103–5
    multiphonic 194–5
    and music 163–4
    in the soma 89–90
speech 3, 4
    and voice 23–4, 32
Spherical Space 93–6
spirituality xiv-xv
Stewart, Rod 69
stomach 12, 174–5
Sufism 124

theatre 162–3
Thoracic Expansion 78, 79–80, 81, 85, 87
thought
    and feeling 13
    and instinct 112–13
throat 13, 113
    constriction 13–16
    stickiness 36–7
trachea 44
Turner, Tina 69
'Twelve Brothers, The' 151
Tyler, Bonnie 69

vocal cords 44–6, 48–9, 51–2, 66, 68, 69, 72,
    83, 134, 167
voice ingredients 43–4, 72
    Articulation 70–1
    Attack 68–9
    Disruption 69–70
    Free Air 66–7
    Harmonic Timbre 56–64, 86
    Loudness 44–8, 82
    Nasality (Violin) 64–6
    Pitch 48–51, 83, 86
    Pitch Fluctuation 51–3
    Register 53–5
Voice Movement Therapy xv-xvi
    Exercises:
    the Animal Matrix 115–17
    the Call of the Heart 8
    Crying Song, Laughing Song 104
    Developing Articulation 71
    Developing Attack 69
    Developing Disruption 70
    Developing Free Air 67
    Developing Harmonic Timbre 61–3
    Developing Loudness 48
    Developing Nasality 65
    Developing Pitch 51
    Developing Pitch Fluctuation 53
    Developing Register 55
    Exploring Areas of Expansion 80
    Exploring Depth 85
    Exploring Frequency 83
    Exploring Pressure 82
    Exploring the Tube 87
    Exploring Volume 84
    the Holding Voice 18
    the Loving Voice 135
    Making Spherical Space 91–3
    the Memory Song 35
    the Prayer Cycle 126–7
    from Prosody to Melody 27
    the Quartet of Passions 184
    the Soul Ballad 156
    the Unspeakable Song 146
    the Vocal Balm 171
    the Vocal Orchestra 167
    Voice Dancing the Sphere 95
    the Voice of Heart and Belly 175
    Warm-up xvii
vowels and consonants 71

Waits, Tom 69
'Wild Swans, The' 151
wipe-out effect 25–7
women's voices 155

Yamana peoples 123
Young, Neil 65